STONEGROUND

A biography of John Rymer, a passionate farming visionary who left a lasting legacy

by Mike Keeble

Stoneground
Copyright © 2008 Mike Keeble, JSR Limited

All rights reserved.

Enquiries should be addressed to:
JSR Limited
Southburn
Driffield
East Yorkshire
YO25 9ED
www.jsr.co.uk

FIRST EDITION
First Printing (June 2008)

Cover Photograph
John Rymer at Givendale

ISBN: 9 780955 947001

Printed in England
www.gkd-litho.com
Designed by www.strawberry.co.uk

John's family, the author and staff of JSR dedicate this book to the younger generations, for whom John intended his Omnium Gatherum, for it is they who will have to face and conquer the growing conflicts of food, energy and a growing population.

Author

Mike Keeble. Farmer in the uplands but with a past in farm management across many types of farming. Now runs under the title of rural commentator as a columnist and feature writer with occasional forays into sound and TV. Talks farming and rural life at a number of different agricultural shows across the country each summer.

This book covers many of his long term concerns for the future as we see good farming practices, such as those John Rymer used so effectively, ignored and misunderstood by politicians and government at a time when our land has to come back to full production in the face of a World population clash with diminishing food and energy resources.

Mike lives in Wensleydale with his wife Peta and has three children, three inlaws and ten grandchildren. Rural Britain is his interest, hobby and the basis of all he does.

Contents

Foreword
By Lord Haskins

John Rymer was one of those people whom, having met once, you never forget. He had many of the characteristics of another remarkably successful person in my life – my father-in-law Alec Horsley who created Northern Foods. He was fiercely committed to whatever he was doing, he was ahead of his times, prepared to take risks when others would not and was very demanding of the people around him. He, as far as I could see, lacked self doubt, even though he claimed he was full of it. He was instinctively anti-establishment but at the same time sought recognition from those in authority. He was endlessly curious. I suspect that he could be easily flattered. His judgement of people was mixed. His style was feudal, which meant that everyone knew their place. If not, you were "beyond the pale". His manner could be dominating and there were times to be frightened of him, but on the other hand if you were in trouble there would be no greater supporter than John. He was a man to go into the jungle with.

All these characteristics meant that he had a special quality which would leave a lasting legacy, and in John's case it was farming. His passion was farming and his single-mindedness made him a remarkable farmer. He knew the detail of every field, walked across them every weekend, knew more about the operations of his huge enterprise than anybody else. His delight in risk taking enabled him to expand when others were more cautious. He always challenged the conventional wisdom, which meant that he was ahead of others in exploring new markets and new ways of doing things. He was a pioneer in potatoes and peas but above all in pig genetics. In this he combined a scientific mind with a competitive business instinct. He was lucky in that he started farming fifty years ago at a propitious time, as subsidies had been introduced to ensure that farmers produced enough to avoid shortages which arose in the recent war. But, whilst he took the subsidies, he felt it important not to rely too much on them – that was why he, and his great friend Tommy Harrison, concentrated on the three unsubsidised markets; pigs, peas and potatoes.

He was a remarkable farmer. He took full advantage of all the latest science and technology to make his fields and his livestock the most productive in the land. But at the same time he had a deep love and respect for the countryside and maintained and enhanced the landscape and its biodiversity by the responsible application of science.

He was more than a farmer. He was involved in setting up several successful business enterprises. Fishers Seeds being the most noteworthy – and he always applied hard nosed business principles to his farming, with the glorious exception of Givendale, which he adored. He was also curious about ideas outside farming and might well have been successful in other spheres of life.

A natural leader, he was also an individualist and a bit of a loner – leadership can be a lonely pastime. There was an element of frustration about him. I always thought he would have liked to have swum in a bigger pond and I am sure he would have succeeded had he done so. But not for him the Presidency of the NFU, an organisation he was always sparring with. He was contemptuous of the politics involved and far too impatient.

I keep coming back to his curiosity – one of the greatest assets of his life. He was curious about markets, about science, about people, about countries – he was a great traveller. He had all the verve, curiosity and daring of a Victorian entrepreneur and empire builder rather than a 20th Century clone from a business school. He would have been completely at home with those amazing people who created the empire, invented modern sport, built the great provincial cities, travelled into the unknown, transformed science and engineering thinking and fashioned the modern world we know today. He would have been a non-conformist Victorian. He also, perhaps, shared their inclination to take themselves too seriously and their humbug. In a peculiar way he was a man ahead of his times, though his roots and his inspiration were clearly fixed in the glorious Victorian era.

John Rymer was a remarkable man who will be remembered for his distinctive contribution to the development of modern British farming.

Overview

In 1983 John Rymer decided to produce his Omnium Gatherum: "Stoneground"; it took him twelve years to complete. Intended for the eighteen grandchildren it was not for anyone outside the family, passing on as it does his experience, wisdom and philosophy of life. It is a remarkable piece of work running to over 600 pages. I have had a unique experience getting right beside John's whole being in a way few biographers will ever have had. I have heard some of his most personal views and frequently I sensed his moods, which has made the man, who I only knew distantly in life, a friend twelve years after his death.

When I was approached by Tim, his son, who now is Chairman of the family firm and Carol, his widow, to produce this book I was entrusted with Stoneground, It has been a great pleasure and privilege to write this book which, in its ending, sums up the huge challenges that face the present generations of farmers..

John Rymer and I were both born to austere non-conformist families in the depressed 1930's when much of the narrow Victorian era still hung on into the 20th Century. We were both City born into families with no rural interest, but circumstances allowed us to roam free into a countryside that was only just awakening to the clamour of internal combustion engines working the earth.

We both had public school educations but as they started to fashion our minds, our genetics and home environments took us down very separate paths, both rural, but with destinations that could not have been more different.

So it was that when I met with Carol and Tim to make our plan I was a small beef and sheep producer with another interest in writing and journalism taking on the life story of one of Agriculture's great food producers.

John had a remarkable brain with a foresight from which he drew his

Stoneground

Master Plan, including his ultimate exit strategy along with family succession, targeted at retirement in 2012 when he would be eighty. He planned to start moving over to let Tim in during his sixties, to keep within reach of the tiller in his seventies and then to spend his closing years enjoying the fruits of his success and watching the family take full command. Well it wasn't like that.

Stoneground was to be passed to the grandchildren in around 2017 when he would be eighty-five and they over forty by which time they would be in full possession of the JSR Group. Tim would be fifty-four, around the age that his father committed his life to paper and indeed father hoped that son would follow his example.

Why Stoneground? He never really explained but there are three possibilities and I like to think he intended it that way.

Without doubt he was a gritty man, determined, fair and reasonable, who could fashion people to suit his needs. That could be one explanation. However he loved the soil on which he farmed in East Yorkshire. Wold land with its own unique blend of loam and flint – stony ground.

And then there was Stoneground, the trading name of a small flour company set up at the back of the family home and run on a part time basis by the gardener. This brought out the romantic in the man. Two ancient sandstone wheels ground the wheat from the Wolds into a wholesome flour: the staff of life.

You can take your pick as you read, but I think the soil made the man who grew the wheat that fed the pigs that in their turn fertilised the land continuing Nature's sustainable cycle. To take this and turn it into a food production business that would influence the world took a man of grit and determination.

Farming is rotational with each element, crop or stock, fulfilling a particular role. John and I lived through a period when agriculture was able to tap energy sources trapped underground millions of years ago as oil and it was consumed at a frightening rate to an identifiable point of exhaustion over our lifetimes. Some say we farmed with two suns, harvesting both.

The Coal, Oil and Gas stored underground were the products of millions of hours of solar energy growing and rotting vegetation. In the 17th Century as the Industrial Revolution gathered pace based around the natural resources of Coal, Water, Wood and Ironstone populations moved from countryside to town. Food was needed to fuel the workforce so farming followed with its own revolution.

In the late 19th Century oil was found and refined to mobile fuels quickly pushing the horse and steam aside. Population continued to climb and around 1930 began to exceed its peak organic capability, but as if in the nick of time inorganic fertilisers, in vast quantities, started to flow from the oil refinery business allowing the food supply to keep up with demand.

When John died in 1996 he knew food production had taken more than its fair share of world resources, he could see the problems that would arise in the future and he would have known that balance had to be restored to farming systems by returning to the more conventional rotations of the past. Growing food is a continuous process traditionally handed on from one generation to the next which is exactly what John most wanted from his family farm in the future.

So when planning this book it soon became clear that JSR created a team of people that he put in touch with the land to produce food and the importance of this was not simply in the immediate success but in the direction the Founder took. He was well aware that forecasts of World Population showed that in around 2035 the people on the planet will have increased by 50% in 30 years, and he also knew that during that time the food production resources of the globe would diminish at a frightening rate.

John would have already been looking forward to this growing conflict and there were others equally concerned. Already it was clear that politicians were only concerned about the short to medium term, long term planning is not a vote catcher. During the months around John's death a group of large food producers, bankers and academics came together to see if they could promote international co-operation to address the erosion of World Fertility and the sustainability in the environment in order that human life could go on without the inevitable conflicts that global food shortages would bring.

1

Growing Environment

On February 22nd 1932 John Sykes Rymer, $8^1/_4$ lbs, was born at The Mount Nursing Home in the City of York. In the same year the baby's father, Arthur, started his engineering business Bootham Engineers specialising in the new technology of welding. Outside the city bounds rural depression ran deep with land being sold at £10/acre and wheat at £4/ton.

The Rymers were one of the City's most prominent families with a long history of civic responsibility. At that time the religious divides were huge with social implications as well. Methodism ran deep in Rymer veins within it the rules of abstinence and simplicity were obeyed and even within the Masonic movement, of which they were part, the Lodges in the City each had a clear denominational bias.

Mary, mother of John, but known to all as Molly, ran the family home in Acomb Road with two servants on a weekly housekeeping allowance of £3, paying the cook/general 35p, in today's currency, with full keep and a washing lady on 10p per day. Out in the countryside wages were dropping below the City average wage of £2.35p per week.

The garden in Acomb Road was John's limited world in early life, he was joined by his brother David in 1935, but all that was to change when in 1939 Arthur built Bachelor Hill, a new house right on the edge of open countryside. It cost £2,302. It was from here that John was set free at the age of seven. In the company of a slightly older neighbour, Tommy Boyd, he explored the surrounding countryside and undertook various landscaping projects in the large garden. Neither he nor his family realised at the time that this was where he took the country road.

John and Tommy were in boys' heaven. Only a short distance away was Askham Bog with otters, dragonflies and birds of many varieties all silently watched as the two friends looked and learnt. Across the fields was Mr Penty's farm where they were always welcome to watch the horses and men at work, "Digging for Victory" in the nation's campaign to rebuild its self-sufficiency after two decades of agricultural decline.

The freedom of those bygone days is hard to appreciate today. Roads were virtually traffic free, rules and regulations were minimal and political correctness didn't exist. John Rymer remembered a quote from "Swallows and Amazons" when a father replied to a request by his children asking for permission to row across a lake to camp on an island, which he did by telegram: "If not duffers will not drown, if duffers better drown." They went.

When the Rymers took up residence at Bachelor Hill War was the dominant force. Petrol rationing, increasing the food supply from British acres, upgrading industry to meet what was obviously going to be a battle fought under the new rules of mechanised militia. Small boys could be left to roam, they had their scrapes, but they survived, gaining an independence and sense of responsibility rarely seen in ten and eleven-year-olds today.

Molly Rymer was concerned for John in his early years for he had a poor appetite, poor digestion, was cack-handed and shy, but as he became increasingly interested in his new surroundings all this changed. As his interests moved away from the bog and increasingly to the farm he saw much less of Tommy Boyd.

On the farm horses were being replaced by tractors sent from the United States to help British farms boost food production. Slowly he became more and more interested in Pat Penty who, of similar age, was to be his close friend and companion for twelve years.

Life was not however just about the farm and wildlife for in the large attic of Bachelor Hill John and David constructed a small theatre with its stage and lighting system. They acquired costumes, wrote plays and as their stagecraft and direction grew so too did their aspirations. Probably their most ambitious production was Goldsmiths 'She Stoops to Conquer' which was acknowledged by the friends, relatives and neighbours who came as a very professional production.

In 1940 with WWII changing practically every aspect of life in Britain John Rymer was sent to St Olaves Preparatory School. He took brother David with him on the Number 8 bus delivering him to Miss Meaby's Kindergarten and then went on to his own school. It was here he met one of his great influences, Mr Wentworth Ping; headmaster, natural history enthusiast who during WWI had been gassed and left to die but regained consciousness when he heard the song of a blackbird on an Ypres dawn. Ping made the outdoors fascinating and through bangs and flashes chemistry exciting.

In 1945 with war over, but austerity still the order of the day, John was sent to Greshams School in Norfolk which had a reputation for encouraging boys to move around independently and to take a special interest in Natural History. An obvious choice, but in later life John looked back with a regret that it had not been more classical and academic.

David followed John to Greshams and Cambridge and then took a teaching diploma at Nottingham. These were two very different peas from the same pod. David progressed from teaching to become Secretary of Advanced Architectural Studies at York University where he became involved with the Northern Arts Council and in the civic life of York following in the family footsteps.

By now Bootham Engineers had grown considerably having been heavily involved in war work and the Rymers of Bachelor Hill were far better off able to join the social and, increasingly, the civic life of the City. Fuel though was in short supply, school trips were out and holiday transport home and back to school was by train.

Looking back it is hard to believe what all this was like. Travel was slow and the trains were over-crowded with huge numbers of service personnel with kitbags, helmets and occasionally guns. Stations were gaslit, gloomy and with no advertising, directional signs or route maps. Soldiers, sailors and airmen returning home at last to peace-time Britain were worn but happy. Young people could travel alone quite safely amongst all the chaos.

Greshams lived up to its reputation allowing John to develop his interest in Natural History, he won the Holland-Martin prize for his study of the biology of a stagnant pool and at weekends he cycled to Blakeney Point on the North Sea shore to study sea birds and plants for the first time.

Team sports, the combined cadet force and general 'house life' held little appeal; he was a loner not a leader.

He became detached from the family with their lives revolving around the social, civic and business life of York. Instead he found his great uncle John Lockwood, a tenant on a farm at Flaxton some distance from York. The farm still relied on horses with men committed to endless hard work but above all to the best possible standards of both animal and crop husbandry. Rymer the farmer had arrived.

Academically he did well at Greshams receiving a place at Cambridge which he took up after his two years' National Service. He left school at seventeen in 1949, took his driving test, which in those days was a brief 20 minute affair, and gained his freedom. At home his parents were content for Arthur had the Company, various directorships and a busy civic and Masonic commitment while Molly played golf and gave her husband maximum support running a comfortable and hospitable home.

Looking back at this first stage of growing up John was very sceptical of the education provided by public schools. He felt it did little to develop the individual's brain; what he went with he left with, with little new added. He certainly had not reached his potential brainpower, but he did nevertheless eventually send his own children through the private system.

He didn't want to leave school at seventeen and await the 'call-up' at the official age of eighteen so somehow he managed to start his military career at a younger age immediately liking the rather hard, healthy and male dominated Spartan life; the uniform gave him a sense of extreme patriotism. He liked that.

Applying for the Royal Army Veterinary Corps, the nearest thing he could find with some connection to farming and wildlife, he first underwent the six weeks' "square bashing" or basic training and from there to RAVC Melton Mowbray HQ, the one remaining equestrian training centre. For the first and last time in his life he fancied the mounted cavalry life but such were the workings of HM Armed Forces he was put onto dog handling.

After learning about the training of dogs to guard and find it was off to Suez, attired in pre-war cavalry breeches, to a country of strange people, crude latrines, rats and flies, but he enjoyed it. This was the start of a lifelong pipe smoking habit originally adopted partly to look the part, but also as an aid agin flies.

Stoneground

Time off was generous, the Mediterranean not far off, swimming he improved, sailing he learnt and on one long leave with no desire to go home, he and a pair of friends toured Egypt and Cyprus finding unspoilt, natural and beautiful places despite the recent ravages of war.

After a year in Egypt it was back home to spend a week's leave with his parents in Woolacombe, Devon. Something he had not done since the early days at Greshams. The hard male military world had changed the public school city boy that Molly and Arthur thought they still had, for now he had become a nineteen-year-old who spoke army talk, had no wish to mix with his family's social group and who made it perfectly plain he preferred his own company. He drank the odd pint, puffed his pipe and at times swore. It was an uncomfortable week for all concerned.

John had entered for and received a pass into the "Wosby" examinations, the War Office Officer Select Board which, if he passed the training course, would qualify him for a commission with obligatory membership of the Territorial Army, but with an early release to take up his place at Sidney Sussex College, Cambridge.

So from Squaddy he passed through the officer training school at Eaton Hall in Chester where the rough edges were knocked off, good manners restored, but when it came to the Officers Mess Codes of behaviour he held back finding the saluting, clubbishness and outright snobbery towards the soldiers he had only just left difficult, if not impossible to accept. This stayed with him in later life.

In August 1951 Second Lieutenant John Rymer of the West Yorkshire Territorial Regiment finished his National Service. In October he entered Sidney Sussex College, Cambridge University a tougher man than the City boy from York now with his own ideas of direction of life if not definition. He wanted to farm and in reality had a lot of learning yet to do. Pat Penty was still by his side having endured the changes from prying little boy from the fringe of York through the public school period and then the toughening up phase now into the pipe-smoking, motor-bike riding undergraduate.

In 1951 Britain celebrated its Great Festival in London and around the provinces. In 1950 Arthur Rymer became Sheriff of York and in the Festival of Britain year he was awarded an OBE for his part in promoting the event and in recognition of his re-introduction of the Medieval mystery plays which signalled the start of a huge growth in the City of York as an international tourist venue. Molly kept pace with her husband with a reputation as an excellent hostess, golfer, bridge player and above all a stylish dresser. In 1955 she was named as one of the 500 Best Dressed Women in Britain. Arthur, although a quiet modest man was rightly proud.

2

The Two Universities

October 1951 was the start of the polishing process of the emerging farmer, but it was not a conventional education. At Cambridge he read Agriculture and so decided to go conventionally rural, which he had never really become. Inspired by his roommate, Chris Godfrey, he bought a shotgun and they jointly founded a Wildfowling Society regularly making forays to the dykes, pools and shoreline lying to the east of Cambridge. His father's allowance of six pounds per week was paid monthly making farm work in the holidays not only educational but an essential expedient to replacing the ancient motorbike he'd bought on leaving the army with a car.

He rowed number five in the Sidney Eight, finally put his interest in the arts behind him and celebrated his 21st birthday quietly with a few friends around a small barrel of Yorkshire bitter reluctantly sent by Arthur who, with Molly, must have been upset that they were not to be included in their son's first step into the 'man's world'.

The varsity vacs were the start of a new dawn. He went to work on a north Norfolk farm owned by the family of one of his close friends at Greshams, Jim Perowne, at the time British farming was becoming prosperous providing heed was taken of the Government's wish to achieve maximum home production of food. Machinery, fertiliser and spray technologies were developing fast and back in the studious atmosphere of Cambridge David Wallace, economics tutor, encouraged John to see all this as a business and not as a way of life as so many aspiring farmers seemed to do in this new era of rural prosperity.

He received a "2.1" BA in Agriculture but hadn't time to receive it formally at the graduation ceremony doing so instead by proxy. He knew he was denying Arthur and Molly the chance of enjoying the pride of attending his degree presentation in the formality of Senate House. It was a gesture of defiance. He had left the fold, left York and was now on his own, but he didn't realise his education was still not yet over.

As President of the Cambridge University Agricultural Society John was responsible for arranging the annual programme of speakers. In the Farmers Weekly, then his regular Friday read, he came across in the farm feature pages Tom Harrison of Burton Pidsea, Hull who he invited to come up and speak on "Pigs, Peas and Potatoes". Harrison agreed to journey from the fertile land of Holderness to the cool academic tranquillity of the University. Tom excited and inspired John for life that evening for he spoke as a good farmer on good land, but he was a businessman first and foremost. He mistrusted the subsidy systems' twisting of market forces persuading as it did crops to be sown because of a subsidy and price guarantee and not in response to a market demand.

Harrison had thought his cropping and stocking through and decided that the average British household ate large quantities of three things not on the subsidy/price guarantee charts; bacon, spuds and canned or dried peas. So his philosophy of Pigs, Peas and Potatoes was born, it proved a winning hand and one that John Sykes Rymer understood as his route into a farm of his own.

That night at Cambridge Harrison too saw an opportunity for here was a young man with foresight and fire. He offered him a job, John took it and in June 1953 unrested from education he and his valiant Royal Enfield 250cc arrived at Chatt House, Burton Pidsea.

Cambridge had taught the thinking and reasoning, it was now the "University of Burton Pidsea" that would hone all that into motivation, ambition and an ability to assess a situation and act upon it within a farming environment. The farming chrysalis would soon emerge as a food producer.

John now got to touch, feel and smell the soil, animals, crops and climate; the ingredients of life to come. Tommy Harrison understood the power of genetics admiring the work of the early 18th Century agricultural improvers such as Bakewell and Townsend who selected the best to breed to the best to achieve better, but over the late Victorian period breeding had been more about line breeding with concentration of families losing the real power, the gift, of hybrid vigour.

So with his pigs Tom crossed Saddleback sows with the recently imported long lean Landrace boars from Denmark. New varieties of crops too were coming available specifically bred for the high value early spud market and for canning peas to go to Batchelor's factory in nearby Hull. Clovers, with their ability to fix Nitrogen into the soil as well as providing a protein rich forage crop, were being both improved here as well as imported from Scandanavia and New Zealand.

These were all constituents in a rotational farming system aimed to maximise profit while maintaining soil health. But the U of B P was not all work and no play.

Tom Harrison had restarted bachelordom, his wife had left, he encouraged his new student who was rather restrained and snobbish at twenty-one to start to work hard and to play as well. Consequently an early engagement to a wealthy farmer's daughter he had met while at Cambridge was cancelled; a Triumph sports car bought along with a sailing dinghy and suddenly new girlfriends appeared. Motor racing, sailing and skiing in the company of new found friends, all with farming roots, set the scene for the final stages of education, growing up and bachelorhood.

In his last year at "UBP" John was put in charge of Oustwick Grange, a 300 acre farm which Harrison and two other farmers had bought as a seed testing station for their latest acquisition J R Fishers, Agricultural Seedsmen of Hull. This was heavy unforgiving land, but once drained and farmed precisely, hitting the soil at just the right moment to achieve a tilth, it could show off varieties of wheat to their full potential.

As 1956 drew to its close and now twenty-four with an ambition to farm a 1,000 acre farm with Pigs, Peas, Potatoes and of course Wheat, John was ready to go it alone. His new girlfriend, Margaret Fleming, an accountant's daughter from Hull, seemed to enjoy the fast life, the ambition, the dreaming of that ideal piece of land and the farmer needs a wife and of course that would mean a family and that all-important next generation.

Around East Yorkshire land was changing hands at £40/acre for a lot of farmers were failing to read the future prospects or to grasp the challenges of new technology and profits were still hard won. A lot of land could be bought but John was set on East Yorkshire or, just possibly, Lincolnshire.

Margaret agreed to be his wife once he found a house and so he started to search in earnest.

Peter Atkinson was the local auctioneer who handled most of the farm sales around Driffield and on the eastern Wolds. It was to him John eventually turned and it was through him that he heard of Eastburn Warren. On the Wold edge, just out of Driffield with 440 acres, an unattractive house devoid of any modern facilities or electricity, but with considerable potential for the three P's: Pigs, Peas and Potatoes.

At £22,000 it was on sale quietly placing it at the top end of the market, but once interest was shown Mr Foster the owner would look no further so time was on John's side as there were now important matters to be attended to. His father agreed to make a £9,000 loan available and one can't help thinking this was from a parent seeking to build a bridge back to a rather arrogant son. From an odd family legacy or two John had £6,000 so with £15,000 he required a mortgage of £7,000 and some working capital – so it was to the bank he went.

His father's bank in York turned him down so he went back to his real home, Burton Pidsea, for a chat to his mentor. Tom Harrison reminded him that one of his new found friends in the village was insurance broker Kenneth Hibbert and from then on the doors all opened. Eagle Star would certainly consider the mortgage and once the farm was ready to buy Barclays in Hull would come up with the £3,500 working capital that John estimated would be needed to farm. However probably for the first and only time in his life he was working on over optimistic budgets for he grossly underestimated what would be needed to make the farmhouse fit for his bride-to-be and of one thing he was sure, the Fleming family would not agree to their daughter's marriage into a house devoid of electricity, hot water, a bathroom, flushing lavatories and a good kitchen.

In March 1957, aged 25, Rymer took up temporary residence at the Queens Head, Kirkburn. His connection with Fishers of Hull meant he could obtain from them "merchant credit" on seeds and fertilisers. He mused while lying in his feather bed above the bar after a hard day's work that there was another P to add to his farming formula: People. Through Tom Harrison he had for the first time become part of a community of people and by working with them, asking advice, he now had his game plan in place.

By 29th June 1957, just four months a farmer, Eastburn Warren had electricity, bathroom, two lavatories, an Aga and three night storage heaters along with £350 worth of furniture mostly from Peter Atkinson's weekly furniture auctions. That day at Hessle Church, the union was made between accountant's daughter Margaret and City businessman's son John. It was the last good day of summer, the pay packets were no more, nor were there allowances from parents: they were on their own and off on honeymoon they went.

In mid July they returned to poor weather, a lot of hard work and for Margaret a new and strange life as a working farmer's wife. For John the overriding thought each evening as he closed the back door on the day was; just 560 more acres to go.

3

Farming Alone

When John arrived at Eastburn Warren it was farmed much as it had been for the past hundred years. The internal combustion engine had only just pushed horsepower to one side and "chemicals" were still seen with suspicion with soil fertility still dependant on good rotational husbandry.

The final act of hand over was not on the day of completion in March 1957 when Harold Foster sealed the deal with a handshake over a silver shilling for the away going crop was still in the ground. This was the final crop on the farm to which the out-goer was entitled and what a crop it was. Bersee wheat, unsuitable for the combine harvester, in need of ripening in the stook, carting, stacking and threshing. It was then stored in sacks until the last day of January 1958 when the crop was sold and collected by a grain merchant. And so the curtains closed on the old and immediately rose on the new.

The fields on the Warren were small, the traditional cropping quite variable reflecting the rotational reliance and John had learnt enough by then to know that changes were needed, but that they had to be gradual and considered in relation both to the land and also to the market. So in his first farming year the cropping was:

> 54 acres Clover Ley to store Nitrogen from the air in the soil.
>
> 56 acres of clover seeds acting similarly.
>
> 25 acres sugar beet, hand pulled to go by train to York.
>
> 20 acres Majestic Potatoes, hand picked, bagged and weighed in the field.
>
> 23 acres of Marrowfat Peas for canning and adding yet more Nitrogen.
>
> 15 acres Swedes for livestock feed.
>
> 75 acres Winter Wheat for feeding stock and flour.
>
> 65 acres Spring Barley.

330 acres of cropping in all with 110 acres of permanent grass, tracks and buildings.

Stoneground

The stocking was 100 breeding sheep and 20 Saddleback sows crossed with a Landrace boar with the gilts reared for sale as breeding stock.

The staff of four men each on £1/day gave a wage bill of £2,000/annum and in his first year John made a profit of £133. However his drawings were £2,560, the mortgage required £750 and he spent £536 on household improvements – a negative cash flow, but the bank was pleased and raised the overdraft to £5,000.

During WWII the UK had become nearly 90% self sufficient, but by 1957 it was falling to below 50% as imported food flooded in. The cry went up from farmers, "Home producer first, Empire second, Foreigners last". The grants on capital improvements, price guarantees and subsidies of the 1947 Agriculture Act were starting to have their desired effect but the National Farmers Union was determined to preserve the small farm and Government concurred. The Small Farms Scheme for holdings from 20 – 100 acres was introduced alongside a proposal to abolish smallholdings below 20 acres but while the former was welcomed the latter was firmly rejected for in Cornwall alone 40% of holdings were less than 20 acres while in East Yorkshire 60% of farms were already over 100 acres. A meeting at the Farmers Club in London simply rejected both ideas as ways of holding farmers back and propping up inefficiency.

This was also a time of change in the pig industry for in 1958 the Danish pig progeny research station stopped 50 years of testing English Large White boars. Their native Landrace had taken over and indeed John Rymer had already gone Danish.

A combination of a shortage of food supplies and a Labour Government desperately trying to refill the empty coffers after a financially punishing war combined to play into the hands of the thinking farmer. The UK balance of payments was way out of kilter making home production as a wall against imports essential and at the same time inflation was running above bank rate. Not only was food production a good prospect for so too was land purchase; the first time this had been the case since the pre-Napoleonic wars around 1815. By 1850 land on the Wolds was at £40/acre for this was the time of "High Farming" much of it boosted by rich industrialists seeking the privacy, privilege and sport that land ownership could bring.

By April 1959 John's dynamics and ambition had taken root on the farm with a profit of £3,842 and drawings down to £1,404. What Norman Fleming, John's father-in-law, thought we know not, but it is certain that for Margaret life would be very hard after the comfort of the Fleming family home in Hessle.

She had a washing machine that could wash 5 lbs of clothes in 5 minutes, but no drier. In farming magazines the women's pages suggested extending "your man's" variety of diet daily, especially in puddings so that he may work harder and for the busy farmer's wife prune and lemon drinks were recommended for health and beauty. Tonic herb beer could be made in batches of 8 gallons for 30p, or two gallon jars of cider for 70p which could considerably reduce the cost of feeding the "hinds" (hired hands).

In December 1958 Margaret was told that her baby due in January would be twins. Baby clothing and equipment had to be doubled up, the farm van was sold and a gleaming Ford Zodiac appeared reflecting John's confidence in his future prosperity.

The £22,000 invested in Eastburn Warren put a capital base down that steadily rose in value enabling more acres to be added and for JSR very quickly to reach and far exceed that original 1,000 acre dream.

Stoneground

Top Left - Delivering the post. In later life John used to say his pipe was the adult substitute for a dummy
Top Right - Filey 1946 aged 14 with mother, brother David and Tim the dog
Bottom - Farfield Senior inter-house Rugby championship 1949. Back row third from left

Stoneground

Top Left - Aged 4 on Filey beach in 1936
Top Right - John's father Arthur in full bathing suit. Perhaps a factor why John preferred naturism in adult life
Bottom - Never quite good enough to get a Cambridge blue John rowed No5 in the Sidney Eight and enjoyed the camaraderie of the rowing club

Private John Rymer of the Royal Army Veterinary Corps at the start of his National Service in May 1950. He progressed to Second Lieutenant of the West Yorkshire Territorial Regiment by the end but was uncomfortable with Officer snobbery towards the troops

Top - In Egypt 1950 the five Great Dane pups Blackie, Brownie, Betty, Ben and Brit (approximately 10 months) and trainers
Bottom Left - With Brownie, a Great Dane war dog in Egypt 1950. Later in life he would reflect that the patience and skill required to train dogs was similar to training people. Time spent with the dog (or an employee) was an opportunity to bond, learn and teach
Bottom Right - Jeff Bowles and the Danes

Dromedary – time off from dog training and all dressed up for camel riding.

The Dog School Fighting Cock

Top - Farfield Prefects 1949 – Back row second from right. Housemaster 'Bird' is middle front row
Bottom - Ready for Sidney Sussex College, Cambridge to read Agriculture – October 1951

Stoneground

Top - Purpose built Solari farrowing house at Eastburn made with engineering bricks in the 60's pig pens
Bottom - Landrace sows being individually hand fed, in dry sow housing at Eastburn in the 60's

Top - Potatoes began to be stored inside in the 60's from the more traditional outside potato pies
Bottom - Hand picking Majestic potatoes in the 60's at Eastburn Warren

Stoneground

Top - Baling with a grey Fergie at Eastburn in the early 60's
Middle - Clearing the Eastburn to Garton road during the severe winter of 1963
Bottom Left - Harold McMillan and John Hornsey harvesting sugar beet at Eastburn in the 60's
Bottom Right - Undersown barley harvested using a Massey Harris combine early 60's

4

JSR Making His Mark

This quarter of a century was an extraordinary period in British agriculture experiencing as it did unprecedented growth through intense technological, mechanical and scientific developments supported by free advice, guaranteed prices on most commodities, subsidies and grants. From the 440 acres of Eastburn Warren the farming business grew to 7,843 acres in 1982 of which 2,992 were tenanted. This remarkable expansion illustrates how John made such an impressive mark on British food production. His lasting message from Cambridge was that farming is a business just like any other, but with Nature as an ally or potential enemy. Through the UBP he learnt the practical application of science and mechanisation which moved him on from the traditional farming of his uncle and he followed the strong work ethic of the Rymers of York. He set his priorities, ultimately that 1,000 acre goal, but to reach there he had to use the accounts to understand the day to day economy, a marketing skill to maximise returns from the unsubsidised pigs, peas and potatoes and, when he had time, to become a farm worker.

In 1961 the first step forward was taken which became one of his most significant when the outdoor sow unit, with its growing market for "blue gilts", went intensive. These Landrace cross Saddleback gilts when crossed with a large White Boar displayed the double dose of hybrid vigour that came from the three-way cross. In 1961 most pigs were bred pure and nearly all breeding stock were kept out of doors where iron was available from the soil thus preventing the killer piglet anaemia, but the introduction of an iron injection at birth allowed farrowing to move indoors reducing death rates and improving growth rates. Sow numbers rose from 20 to 100, the natural grazing Saddleback went to be replaced by Landrace sows mated to a Large White boar. In turn carcase quality improved as the high body fat from the Saddleback went out of the equation.

In 1964 John made his first move towards expansion when he purchased 130 acres at Huggate for £130/acre, in just seven years land prices had doubled. At around this time Sir William Prince-Smith of Southburn House was reducing his estate, but when his 180 acre Town Farm at Huggate, came up to re-let he offered it to JSR Farms who then were farming 770 acres. In 1968 he could have bought the Catwick Farm lock, stock and barrel, for £200/acre but this was a 500 acre farm and he took the cautious approach of a tenancy. Here he took over 200 outdoor Saddleback sows, a 180 ewe flock and also a sugar beet quota. This was a good farm with some very good light land. Bill Robinson had worked on the farm since leaving school, he became one of John's vital managers, a man with energy and enthusiasm who knew the importance of timeliness at such times as sowing and harvest.

John regretted not buying this farm but added 245 acres to it in later years.

Virtually from the start John had brought in Harold MacMillan as his farm foreman at Eastburn Warren emphasising the fourth P of people and they worked very closely together over 32 years and it was to Harold that John entrusted the initial training of many young men over the years knowing that under his tutorship they had every chance of becoming key players in the expanding business. As each new farm came up for consideration Harold's opinion was taken.

When John took the farm at Huggate he also acquired Norman Wood as his foreman to run the 398 acres. Neither man could have realised at the time just what was in store for those early '60's were years of great change in land ownership, very similar to the 'high farming' period 100 years previously when large estates were set up using industrial wealth and this was when the Southburn Estate had been acquired by West Riding of Yorkshire industrialists; the Prince-Smith family. In 1969 Sir Richard Prince-Smith decided to move to the USA as optional taxation started to bite. As a result his Agent put 2,000 acres at Haywold, to the west of Eastburn, on the market at £300/acre. John had tried to persuade them to let him take the tenancy, but the Halifax Estate purchased the farm and then offered JSR Farms the chance of a joint venture which allowed the new owner to take rent as earned income thus avoiding the penal tax on unearned income which was slowly eroding away capital on many large rented estates.

John Rymer was Managing Director of Haywold Farms Ltd but he was never happy over the twenty year life of the Company as he alone was not in total control. He was though now farming over 4,000 acres, he was thirty-seven years old and took it all in his stride. Only five months later Sir Richard Prince-Smith made a direct approach to John, he had arranged to let the Southburn Home Farm to his farm manager, but he had got cold feet and given back-word. One thousand more acres for £10/acre – John couldn't say no. So in a dozen years the target had been exceeded by 4,000 acres – he was now over 5,000, but he was not altogether happy as a large proportion, Haywold and Southburn, were not owned.

He only had four years to wait before Lady Luck once more turned his way. In 1974 he was offered vacant possession of Southburn, Sir Richard wanted his money out, but John Sykes Rymer was at his limit, the price seemed high at £400/acre and he had until December 31st to say yea or nea.

On Christmas Eve he drove to Victoria Pier on the Humber at Hull, this was before the Humber Bridge, to meet the ferry from Lincolnshire bringing Geoff Cooper, the agent for Southburn, to see if a deal could be done. Such was the wish of both parties to agree hands were quickly shaken on the deal whilst sitting in the car leaving Cooper to get back on the ferry and John to go and join his good friends Kenneth Hibbert and Tommy Harrison for their traditional lunch. That was indeed a moment for celebration for the successful farmer and his two mentors and friends. He had just played for high stakes and won.

When John had taken the tenancy of Southburn he and Margaret moved into the main estate house, but now it was theirs and it was at this point that John felt he had really arrived, but such was his quiet and modest personality that his satisfaction at becoming a substantial landowner, not simply as a farmer, was not allowed to show through. Nevertheless at Southburn House he really put down his roots making it the family home and the family Company H.Q.

Out on the farms Harold MacMillan and Norman Wood were

adjusting well to the continual expansion. During that momentous year of 1974 Norman had a further 1,000 acres of tenanted land at Givendale, adjacent to Haywold, added to his responsibilities.

Back in 1969 John had head hunted Malcolm Pearson, an advisor from the local Ministry of Agriculture Office in Beverley, as Livestock Director of JSR Farms Ltd and it was he who under the guvnor's direction set to work to build the pig business. He was to work for the Company for the next 23 years. At the same time it was becoming clear that the office was becoming complicated with the danger it could so easily slip into chaos, such was the pressure on management time. In 1970 John advertised for a Commercial Director to control the finances and introduce business management at the Southburn H.Q. He well remembered his economics tutor David Wallace's words as he left Sidney Sussex, "John, see farming as an industry, study business management, for it is the key to your future." He was then 21 he was now 38.

Another 2,000 acres was to be added to JSR Farms over the next 8 years. Decoy Farm in the Driffield area, 631 acres in 1976 then in 1981 they jumped the Humber to Caenby Corner on the Lincolnshire Wolds with 866 acres and then in 1982 back to the home climes with 542 acres at Gomary added to the Company's property portfolio.

In the Royal Agricultural Society of England's 1982 Annual Journal John wrote about the dawn of Computer Agriculture. In 25 years he now farmed 7,000 arable acres with a small beef and sheep interest, ruminants having little appeal. However his 2,000 sows were becoming World Class. In the article he states three reasons for his success. First lowland prices coinciding with cheap money. Second excellent managers doing the farming in the field backed by hard working directors at H.Q. Third his reliance on the back of an envelope never resorting to a calculator, bearing in mind his office accounting practices at the time were not entirely accurate. He stressed the problem of knowing which figures could be relied upon when making major policy decisions. Did you rely on the foremen who were the managers in the field or the analysis of accounts in the office, for the two did not always give identical answers. Working with the National Institute of Agricultural Engineering he was sure that computer technology would be a certain way forward and JSR Farms were already moving in that direction.

The farms were thriving, the pig business expanding both at home and abroad, but back at home all was not well, sadly his marriage had worn out. He had worked hard, making sure Margaret and the five children had everything they wanted, he went on super holidays with them, but that all essential warmth, touch and love had gone. Friendship was not enough.

By June 1980 the original target had been exceeded five-fold, and John was by then non-executive Chairman of both the family company, Bootham Engineers, and Fisher-Thompson (seeds and grain). He was Operations Director of the Driffield Pea Co-operative and, in addition, held three advisory posts on Government committees. His nose was on the grindstone, his energy was extraordinary, at home far less and less time and he made the excuse it was just business as usual, but his marriage had floundered. It was time to act and his first step was to analyse life as it was. As Chairman and Managing Director of JSR Farms he calculated that in a 300 day working year he spent 66.66% of his time, or 200 days, being a farmer, 25% at Bootham and Fishers, 5% on Peas and 3% on Government committees.

It was clear this could not go on without some revision particularly as the business was still growing and likely to go on doing so. He realised that management was the key and that by bringing training to the fore within Company philosophy it could be made more efficient, more reliable and he hoped increasingly home grown.

John and Margaret finally parted in 1981, she to a farmhouse only a few miles away which became the girls' base. Tim at eighteen was gaining practical experience on other farms having decided, much to his father's relief, that he would join the family firm, so he remained at Southburn. This could have been a time for the Chairman to drift having shaken off the worry of being the wrong husband, but he didn't, instead he found new energy, got to know Tim much better and they had fun together as well as having time to discuss the future.

In 1982 John celebrated his fiftieth birthday by writing what he called "Perception in Boots" once more referring to the vision of himself as the muddy booted Farmer, which he never really was. His aim was to identify the cultural mysteries of a confused society so that he might use this to advantage over the rest of his life. He was fifty and single.

Looking back on the failure of his education to develop the wider mind it took a long time, with the help of Kenneth Hibbert, to find literature as a constructive recreation ultimately leading to happiness. When he was confirmed at Gresham's the sole canon he took from it was to love one's neighbour – he felt he got little else from it.

From his success as a farmer he had become wealthy and felt guilty because of it, but when he saw the wealth creating a healthy flow of tax to the State and security to the family, employees and shareholders he felt happier.

He noted how he hated the elitism which he saw so much of in the county set, pony club, public schools and the Officers Mess. Western civilisation too came in for his disapproval as he saw it as being propelled by its own commercial success thus reducing the quality of life it purported to improve.

When he was offered Southburn in 1975, initially as a tenant, he fell in love with the confluence of Southburn and Eastburn Becks and in the evening to look west to the setting sun, to Tibthorpe where Margaret lived, then on to the rising Wolds was to him sublime. He became the custodian of his land at that point determined not to build up primitive territorial ambitions.

He felt he had failed his family and lost his confidence, he needed desperately to find the real JSR again. He concluded that happiness is best defined as appreciation without stress and so he sought to become a universal man, the opposite of which are specialists, experts or consultants who get blinded by the sheer complexity of a narrow field on which they advise other narrow specialists.

Jesus of Nazareth was the Universal Man; the perfect management consultant.

Speaking at a banking conference in 1983 John emphasised how, despite being seen as a big business with assumed factory methods, his farms had a rotational system which minimised agro-chemical inputs and his goal was top quality of every product grown on the farms which was achieved by constantly using improved genetics.

Stoneground

He concluded by saying that in 2000, when he would be sixty-eight, U. S. scientists were forecasting that climate change would become apparent due to increased CO_2 levels. If so the Wolds could well warm up and he would move into pineapples and coconuts as a challenge in old age. However on a serious note he stressed that there would be an increasing demand for carboniferous raw materials either to eat, process or burn and this could be grass, grain, roots or oilseed and so long as the genetics create a crop with low enough costs of production to allow for profit then all would be well. "Farm land will have to take over as oil and gas runt. Farmers will adapt and speed up the natural processes initiated by the sun. Farmers have to get used to the fact that they will become both energy and food producers."

One day John went to Driffield Market, a rare occasion, and he met Peter Atkinson the auctioneer and the man who had helped and advised in the purchase of that first farm Eastburn Warren.

"Hello, John, this is a rare pleasure. What brings you here?" Peter asked.

"The rain" John replied, "We can't get on a spray, the wheat's got rust and this is no weather to bring on good crops – so here I am."

"How are the family?"

"Oh – very well."

"Well that's all that matters then."

Wasn't it? John often drew on that simple exchange in later life when he knew the business was taking him over.

5

Carol

John's marriage ended in 1981, his social life changed, he met new people and renewed old friendships. The pig business had been growing continuously as the farmed acreage increased, the name of JSR was synonymous with quality breeding stock. In 1982 it was decided to define their proven pigs by using the name Healthbred.

The acreage farmed went on growing with the addition of the tenancy of Gomary Farm near Beverley which was to run with Decoy Farm and in 1985 483 acres at Skerne near Driffield were purchased.

In 1983 Lord Halifax asked John to raise £25,000 from the local farming community for the Cancer Relief Fund in aid of Macmillan Nurses. The two of them were in business together on Haywold but they were very different people in every way. John was unfazed by His Lordship's request, seeing it really as a challenge and in the event raised over £53,000 by asking local farmers to give a ton of grain at harvest. The support he got was outstanding and he was content in the knowledge that the challenge had been well and truly met.

In 1984 he became President of the National Pig Breeders' Association which gave him easy access to the leaders in the pig industry at a time when JSR Healthbred was becoming a world leader.

During the period of bachelordom he became increasingly involved in the Merchant Adventurers of York following a long family tradition. From Junior to Senior Warden then on to Deputy Governor. This important and ancient guild was in financial trouble, it needed new energy and time to bring it back on an even keel.

The wonderful medieval hall was in urgent need of restoration, facilities needed updating so that better catering could be introduced. Without all this and new interpretation revenue from visitors it would just keep going down. In his Governor's Year from 1983 – 1984 he attended over twenty-five ceremonial occasions at other Guild Companies in other cities. At the time of his senior office he was very proud to admit Tim into the Company to continue the long family tradition.

Throughout this period John frequently met Carol Brand who had been widowed in 1979. Only thirty-nine and with a son and daughter she had picked herself up and gone into partnership with a friend starting a catering company; Parties Unlimited, which was a great success.

Their friendship grew and in early 1985, atop an ancient lighthouse on Denis Island in the Seychelles, he proposed. She accepted and on 17th April they were married. He was fifty-three. Carol put the missing links into John's life by wanting to be involved in all he did, fostering a love of the countryside, but above all being someone he could be close to and confide in.

The new Mrs Rymer had the genes and life experiences that mattered. The daughter of a successful Hull industrialist, educated at a public school which she enjoyed, excelling at sport and after a commercial course in London she returned to the family firm. She married one of her father's rising stars Chris Brand, who sadly died after just 18 years of marriage. They had two children Giles (1964) and Cathie (1966).

Carol was a good cook, she had been in catering and once married, after only a one night honeymoon at the Savoy, she returned to Southburn House with instructions to give it a real going over.

She took immediate interest in a small stone-ground flour company, learnt quickly about the JSR pig company and brought the lot together in a series of cookbooks publishing three volumes in 1989, 1991 and 1993.

John quickly realised he now had a partner who could interpret the food he produced to the consumer, who moved socially through all classes and types, whose good looks and manner brought publicity and acknowledgement. He was inspired.

Carol also brought two other things into John's life. He had always enjoyed the landscape firstly as a child at Batchelor Hill and later on the land he farmed and Carol brought this to a new height by encouraging more tree planting and having a greater say on what went on in Southburn Garden.

John had never been a sportsman apart from an oarsman at Sidney Sussex. Carol came from a family who were cricket aficionados mixing at both County and International level, she inherited her father's love of leather on willow passing it on to John and to the surprise of many he took to it like a duck.

In his Omnium Gatherum John describes his wedding. After a Civil Ceremony in Beverley Registry Office the couple's sons, Tim and Giles, drove them over the Wolds in brilliant weather to a service and reception in the chapel of the Medieval Merchant Adventurers Hall in York. He probably illustrates just how much his marriage was going to mean when he mentions a line from a poem, The Dream, "Dear Love, for nothing less than thee".

This was to be his turning point with new energy, new ambition and new ideas which he summed up as an introduction to the Carol Era: "At fifty my second life begins as I discover the true quality of country life as I busily forge my strategy for farming in the 1990's".

6

The Family

The Rymer family grew to seven at Eastburn Warren with the twins Jane and Sally arriving in January 1959 with only a few weeks' warning that they were to be two. Timothy followed in November 1963 then came Belinda in March 1965. Six years on as the move to Southburn House was fast approaching came a surprise and Rebecca was born in January 1971.

Life changed for John and Margaret over those 14 years. When they returned from their honeymoon to a starkly furnished house, a farm truck and 440 acres the dream was of 1,000 acres yet when Rebecca came along JSR Farms was looking after 5,000 acres and an international pig business was taking root setting in motion yet another ambitious target.

In 1957 the Driffield Players became a focal point into which they both threw enthusiasm as an escape from the rigours of establishing a modern farm from one that had stood still for a long time. Bill Hayley and his Comets set the music world alight with Rock Around The Clock and the dimly lit rock parties of the '60's arrived to the music of Cliff Richard, Lulu, the Beatles and many a smooch was had to the strains of Bridge Over Troubled Water and Moon River.

As the children arrived John's life was gathering pace and he saw less and less of the family, but holidays were always made exciting active events when they could all be together.

All the children went to public schools, a system in which John had misgivings, which may well be why they all went to different schools. He didn't like the cultivation of upper class aspirations and lifestyles knowing that part of his success was in his community being as much as possible on level terms. When making his first choice, for the twins who had experienced the upper class attitudes at their preparatory school, he and Margaret opted for a strict Wesleyan Methodist school in Hertfordshire. Such was its teaching success that both Jane and

Sally have a deep and lasting commitment to a Christian way of life.

Belinda was sent north to Gordonstoun as John was attracted by the co-ed principles of the German headmaster who believed fresh air and adventure were integral to a good education, but it didn't seem to work and once more the upper class influences came through.

Tim followed his father and Uncle David to Greshams and Rebecca, who had always been somewhat isolated from her siblings and after following her sisters through Foremarke, the prep school for Repton, went to the Quaker school in York, The Mount.

When John was at Greshams the masters were the product of Victorian parents and it showed through in the whole attitude to education. By the time his children went into "the system" he reflected on his own experiences comparing them with those he then experienced as a parent and he concluded that education was still failing its students. This comes through very much in the "in house" training and education that the JSR company quickly built into its management systems in the future.

Over his crowded lifetime John somehow found time to develop serious interests in philosophy, painting and poetry. As a boy he and David built a theatre in the attic presenting quite difficult productions and it was all this that John felt education was missing.

In his Omnium Gatherum John reflects on school where sport and the Combined Cadet Force played such a large part. He was not a team sportsman, he didn't like to be ordered what to do, neither was he a spectator. To him, sport, and cadetship, was about co-ordination and self discipline concluding that cricket probably required more concentration than anything else and we were so good at it because of British Perseverance, the straight bat and rule book which lost us an Empire but won two World Wars.

When he wrote that little did he know just how much cricket would feature in his future.

7

1985 to 1996

The happiness that John and Carol shared lasted just over 11 years. When they were married in 1985 John was completing his year as President of the National Pig Breeders Association, which had given him access to people who mattered in the narrowing world of pig production. The endless trips and meetings could now be put aside so that he could concentrate on home, the farms and his new partner.

He only accepted invitations to join committees if they were to have a beneficial role for his business.

In 1965 he became Chairman of the Driffield branch of the National Farmers Union and County Chairman of the Pigs Committee. The following year he became a Commissioner of Taxes sitting at Bridlington. In 1969 he was elected Chairman, for a year, of the Driffield Conservative Association a job he enjoyed as it gave him the chance to destroy the myth of Tory champagne in large country houses. In 1984 he became Chairman of Kirkburn Parish Council.

However it was involvement with farming organisations he most wanted to be a part of so he was pleased when asked to join the "War Ag" soon after he arrived at Eastburn Warren. This was a Government body that had overseen the WWII push for food production and it soon came to an end to be replaced by specialist Advisory Committees to the Ministry of Agriculture. He was duly elected to MAFF's High Mowthorpe Farm Panel which concerned itself with the work of the experimental and demonstration centre for the improvement of Wold farming. Soon he joined the National Soils Advisory Group, a subject very dear to him, under the Chairmanship of Sir Nigel Strutt and their final report, in 1970, warned of the dangers of mono-cropping that in most cases would cause compaction of soils by heavy machinery which would have such a damaging effect on UK soil structure and its potential production.

He moved on to Chair the Research Council's cultivations panel as

29th June 1957 – John and Margaret were married at Hessle Church

Top - Kenneth Hibbert and Tommy Harrison outside Chatt House, Burton Pidsea in 1948 two influential friends and mentors in John's early career

Bottom - Quod Erat Demonstrandum – Impending marriage, the purchase of Eastburn Warren and flipping the TR2 put an end to a brief period of fast living at the University of Burton Pidsea

Top - The farmhouse was only just ready after John and Margaret return from honeymoon in July 1957 – at least two indoor lavatories had replaced the outside one
Bottom Left - Returning to open a garden fête for Tommy Harrison at Chatt House, Burton Pidsea 1958
Bottom Right - Starting to grow into the farmer businessman

Clay pipe draining at Decoy in the 80's with Tony Arnot

Top - Potato planting in the 70's. The length of the chits suggest a mild winter. Cold and hard work for the indominable ladies
Bottom - Straw burning on the Yorkshire Wolds in the 70's – not the good black burn that John required to kill noxious weeds and slugs

Stoneground

Top - Of all the crops sugarbeet challenged John the most. Not an ideal land for top yields he was constantly disappointed to be below his friend Pat Nutt in the British Sugar League Table. Sugarbeet top silage was made to feed to the lowland beef units
Bottom - Silage making from a one year ley to feed the dairy cross Charolais beef animals housed on lowland units

Top - The move to Southburn in 1971 gave John an opportunity to convert the Prince Smith family holiday flat into JSR offices
Bottom - Ewes and lambs caught out in a spring snowfall at Givendale

Stoneground

Top - JSR hosted the 1976 Potato Harvesting demonstration at Southburn
Middle - Trailed FMC pea viners replaced static viners as East Yorkshire became an important area for frozen pea production
Bottom Left - The first self propelled FMC pea viner helped to revolutionise the speed and cost of pea vining
Bottom Right - Harold McMillan – there from the beginning – a loyal, hardworking and proud Scotsman. A chain-smoker who delighted and exacerbated JSR in equal measure. He became a mentor for Tim in his later life

Top - Haywold Mill grew as the pig business grew and was part of the JSR philosophy. Growing wheat as cheaply as possible, milling it themselves, feeding it to their pigs and then selling added value breeding stock. Regulation caused it to close in 1993 and the Company to outsource to National Compounders

Middle - John's pipe was put to many uses. Biting through the stem when he was cross was a regular occurrence. A missing sugarbeet cotyledon is demonstrated here

Bottom Left - Eastburn Warren (background) – irrigating potatoes on the gravel

Bottom Right - Norman Wood on Haywold with fiddle drill. A legend at JSR who inspired immense loyalty from his staff and had a special relationship with John. He regarded time away from running Haywold, the Mill and the transport fleet as a waste of time, preferring time off to rear his pheasants

Stoneground

" ---- quick as y'can Vicar, - we've got yous lambin'
at Givendale, spuds to plant at Haywold, peas to drill
on Southburn, beet to drill at Catwick, wheat
to spray ----------- "

APRIL 17th 1985

Top - John and Carol on their wedding day in the grounds of the Merchant Adventurers Hall, York where they had their marriage blessed by the Reverend Jack Armstrong

Bottom Left - Philip Huxtable editor of the JSR Newsletter captured the moment perfectly in the Spring 1985 edition

Bottom Right - Carol helped to reignite his passion for painting which formed part of the routine of the day on Denis

Market scene with Carol in foreground by John Rymer

Stoneground

Top - Beach on Denis by John Rymer
Bottom Left - Still dictating letters at the airport but even John couldn't prevent himself completely switching off on the beautiful Denis Island, Seychelles
Bottom Right - JSR Healthbred was moving from a farming company producing pigs to an international genetics business

Top Left - A real switch off – a catch from the River Spey in July.

Top Right - If you stayed at Southburn House between Christmas and Easter you usually ended up planting a tree

Bottom - In the 70's the UK imported all its hard wheat for milling from countries such as Canada. John responded to the challenge by setting up Southburn Wholemeal flour to evaluate UK varieties. Hector Robinson – the man for all seasons (pictured foreground) supervised the monthly production run. Nobody understood what 'untreated' meant (see board behind mill) because the wheat got the same 'treatment' as the rest of the farm!

Stoneground

Company of Tobacco Pipe Makers & Tobacco Blenders   18th October, 1983

    The Master of the Worshipful Company of Tobacco Pipe Makers and Tobacco
Blenders, Mr. Derek Merton, very kindly invited a fellow pipe smoker to join him
and Company at a dinner with the Lord Mayor, Dame Mary Donaldson, and the City
Sheriffs in the Mansion House. London's Mansion House is a fine old building on
which money has recently been spent in restoration. The Egyptian Hall provides
a superb setting for the dinner at which ladies were present. Sally, my
daughter was able to accompany me and to share the generous hospitality provided
by one of the oldest craft Gilds in the City whose members today still represent
the great names in the tobacco industry.

Top - The Wholemeal Flour enterprise was more R&D than a business. In the end new hygiene regulations forced it to close
Middle Left - 1983 – John's year as Governor of the Merchant Adventurers at the Charter Day Court
MIddle Right - One of John's favourite invitations during his year as Governor of the Merchant Adventures (1983) – the
worshipful company of tobacco pipe makers and tobacco blenders. A bachelor again, at the time, daughters Sally and Jane was able to
accompany him for many of the invitations during the year

Top - He knew every acre he farmed employing a sixth sense to find troublespots and/or machines broken down
Middle Left - Divine Worship on a Sunday morning on the Southburn tennis court. From left to right – Dr Jimmy Low, John, Carol and Michael Shepherdson
Middle Right - Tennis on Denis. John and Carol with Marylyn who John described as a streak of chocolate lightening on the court
Bottom - Carol, her sister Mary Rose and their Macmillan Team launched the Southburn Christmas Fayre in 1994, it has become such an important calendar event that it has now moved from Southburn to the Kelleythorpe Showground

Stoneground

Top - John organised a Victorian farm Sunday to raise money for cancer research. Full scale steam powered threshing was on show with local farmers providing the labour. Pictured here are Pat Nutt (middle foreground) and Derek Megginson (right)
Bottom Left - In 1991 JSR Healthbred won the Queens Award for Export
Bottom Right - In a bid to encourage more people to eat British pork Carol produced a number of cookbooks with recipes from family and friends

well as the Letcomb Laboratory for the Agricultural Research Council also serving on the Arable and Forage Crops Board.

1985 was a time of milk and wine lakes, cereal mountains and sugar dunes, EU/CAP over-production, which antagonised the consuming public who saw farmers getting rich on subsidies raised from their taxes. Harvest that year was grim but it didn't stop John crossing the River Humber to buy a Lincolnshire brash farm at Caenby Corner. He admitted privately that it was a decision against his better judgement. Borrowings were at £2.5 million, the accounts were on track, the bank were happy, but something had changed and it may have been that his thoughts were on other personal commitments.

In 1986 after many months of talks he successfully negotiated the sale of the family company Bootham Engineers to a plc, Dowding & Mills and the family became substantial shareholders in the new company as a result. During that year he introduced profit sharing at management level throughout JSR and in his year end report he was able to announce that JSR Healthbred had doubled its sales showing a profit of £148,000 and as a result the pig interests became a target for takeover by the remaining pig breeding companies. What a change from the old days when hundreds of pedigree breeders with their variety of breeds had supplied breeding stock for thousands of small farmers who supplied the country's pork and bacon.

By 1986 Fishers Seeds, of which John was Chairman and major shareholder, reached a handling capacity of 85,000 tonnes of grain putting it in the big time but not in the big international trading pool. He decided the time was right to move out and a sale was quickly agreed to Associated British Foods for £6 million. Once more the family benefited.

In 1988 the land bank increased, but now at prices way above the purchase of that first farm. Swaythorpe Farm, a 758 acre farm came on the market. This was one of the best pieces of Wold earth to be found, John loved it, he had the funds to bid strongly and finally settled for £1,915 per acre. Shortly after this 199 acres at Gomary was bought for £2000/acre. JSR Healthbred was still being stalked by the competition.

A year on in 1989 the decision was made to float JSR Healthbred as an independent Company. To set the scene a company, WFP/Bibbys with 2,000 sows was acquired, giving the new company 10,000 sows, a strong breeding base on which to build an International Company. A joint Company in Western Germany was started and JSR Healthbred became a truly international pig operation confirming John's commercial determination and aggression towards his competitors, "OK come after me."

In that year Tim was married to Jane and John recorded a typical day in the life of he and Carol which shows the shared routine they had adopted around each other's independent lives and responsibilities. Awake at 6.10am to tea and the early morning farming programme on Radio 4, now on at 5.45am! Bathing, shaving, bed making and breakfast at 7am with home baked bread from Southburn stoneground flour. Instructions given to Hector, their man for all seasons; garden programme, pool and court maintenance, cars to fill and prepare. Away to the office at 8am for John and a little later Carol left for Hull Magistrates Court where she was Chairman of the Bench. After a short Court programme and a busy time in the office they both returned to Southburn for home baked rolls and coffee followed by a field/crop walk on one of the farms.

Return to Southburn at 4pm, John back to the office, Carol to the house to prepare for a tennis supper at 6.45pm. Twice a week at 9.15pm John would head for Driffield swimming pool for his back therapy of swimming, returning home at 10pm for a glass, occasionally two, of J & B whisky. Justini and Brooks to John were his elixir of life.

In his words, "It's life in overdrive keeping a lot of people happy not least our parents, but it's a good rewarding life requiring 'switch off breaks' to avoid the risk of simply becoming activity machines lacking sympathy and attention to detail".

In 1990 JSR Farms were farming over 9,000 acres, JSR Healthbred carried on its expansion with the acquisition of a pig A.I. centre in nearby Selby as well as starting a joint venture in Spain. The Company was now Number 3 in the EU pig world.

John had always maintained a dialogue with the big retailers, in particular Marks & Spencer who he saw as his target for Company quality and service. He was relieved, if somewhat triumphant, when M&S dropped their organic campaign in that year. He had little time for the growing talk of organics, not least by Government. Probably the most satisfying sale of the year was 11,500 breeding gilts delivered to West Germany.

In 1991 the genetic superiority of both Healthbred's dam and sire lines was rewarded by having the opportunity to link into the world's largest pig market in the U.S.A. In September the link was announced between JSR Healthbred and DeKalb, the largest pig breeding company in North America.

In that same year JSR Healthbred received the Queens Award for Exports which was presented by the Lord Lieutenant Tony Bethell at a ceremony at the Southburn HQ. An appropriate accolade to John Rymer and his hard working team.

For his 60th birthday present John resolved that he and Carol would in future take two escapist holidays annually, naturally to tropical sun-soaked islands. So from 1992 they did just that.

In that year, 1992, the pig company was getting a lot of adverse attention from the Animal Rights Movement. John was appalled as he had always put welfare at the top of the list when planning and designing facilities for livestock, buildings or transport and they were now recognised as exemplars operating within a worldwide marketplace.

On November 14th 1992 the early morning paper delivery man noticed a fire in the Southburn HQ, the offices had been ransacked, the fire started and petrol containers placed nearby which in the event failed to ignite. The alarm was quickly raised, the fire extinguished, but a lot of damage had been done. Some time later John accepted an invitation to address the Women's Farmers Union Animal Welfare Seminar, which gave him an ideal opportunity to take to a national platform to rebuke the Animal Liberation Front..

But 1992 will not be remembered just for that, for this was the year of the return of John Major to Number 10, the UK left the ERM and in September the financial world collapsed on Black Wednesday. British Coal just closed most of its pits and the UK experienced a 20% devaluation brought about by a floating exchange rate.

Stoneground

It was also the year of compulsory Set A Side which took fertile cereal land out of production confirming to John the lack of understanding of the world agricultural situation by the Eurocrats in Brussels. On the 9,000 acres of farmed land hundreds of tonnes of Wheat were foregone but the rising costs of conservation of the one year grass leys that formed part of the cropping cycle was withdrawn from the rotation partially replacing the crop foregone.

Despite national gloom the Company declared a pre-tax profit of over £2 million on a turnover of £14 million with an overdraft of £1.75 million meaning that for every one pound borrowed there were £12 of assets.

The 1993 summer matured into the wettest harvest ever remembered ruining what had promised to be a record harvest. Grain had to be cut at up to 30% moisture, drying costs were high and quality was poor. Two extra potato harvesters costing £70,000 had to be purchased, pigmeat crashed in value. As the year came to an end John was very pleased when Chris Haskins, Chairman of Northern Foods, accepted an invitation to join the Board as a non-executive Director.

JSR Farms' emphasis on training went across all levels of the Company and I say more about this later. In the autumn of 1993 the top management team met to debate change in adjusting and adapting the farming system to oncoming legislation. They were also asked by the Chairman to examine the future personnel structures. Could they be more efficient and hence more profitable?

Such was their confidence in "The JSR Way" that they decided to market JSR Farms as a contractual service to other landowners. This would capitalise on their management skills, spread the fixed costs of production and offered the possibility of improving market values of quality crops.

1994 was memorable for John and Carol when they realised that in the previous nine years they had spent nine months in the Seychelles together – so far. They looked forward to many more. At around this time John accomplished something he'd hankered after for some time, in fact, ever since tractor driver Brian Hebblewhite made his first archaeological find which led to the start of the Southburn

Archaeological Collection. He commissioned an archaeological survey by Gail Falkingham of seven of the farms which showed a continuous agrarian community living and working on the Wolds for over 2,000 years. From this he gained great satisfaction, reinforcing his belief that farmers are custodians passing on natural resources to the next generation.

Tim was appointed M.D. of the arable division which, at the age of thirty-one, was a tribute to his diligence and hard work over the past 10 years since leaving university. He would be farming the 9,500 acres which were supporting JSR Healthbred pigs, now number 3 in Europe and employing 195 people.

In 1994 Carol was appointed Deputy Chairman of Hull Magistrates Bench, a large Court requiring 160 JP's to operate efficiently and it was the first year that Carol, with her sister, ran the Southburn Charity Christmas Fayre collecting £6,000 in one day for the benefit of the Hull Hospice.

John was very enthusiastic about promoting the idea of contractual farming, but he wasn't alone as a number of other individuals and organisations with arable expertise were exploiting the benefits of scale. Suddenly this was a crowded marketplace in which not all the players were working from accurate costings. Quiet chaos ensued.

In1995 John reflected on the past and was extremely glad that JSR had never been tempted down the monoculture, all cereal, route instead maintaining one third of the cropping area, 3,000 acres, in break cash crops. Just as in their livestock interests all of the crops grown had advanced genetics and budgeted yields were nearly double those used back in the early days.

A large proportion of the wheat and barley grown was by now going as feed into the pig units where a 250 sow unit was producing the equivalent of 30 tonnes of artificial fertiliser, sufficient to grow 100 acres of wheat.

It was in 1995 that John Rymer started to get concerned about world population and the food producing resources necessary for the world to be sustainable. As he applied his philosophical mind to the problem one conclusion was that "Sustainability has become an incomprehensible catchword born of an unscientific public conviction that farmers are degrading the eco-system. Balanced rotational cropping will ultimately prove to be both profitable and environmentally acceptable". Looking at this statement in 2008 no sounder warning could have been given, but this was made in the privacy of his O.G.

The Company accounts in 1995 reflected the excellent weather conditions of 1994 exceeding the budget put in place in late 1993. Despite JSR Healthbred (breeding pigs) showing a loss of £0.5 million, pig production (pigs for the meat market) made £0.7 million and the arable division £1.5 million. With a £20 million investment the pre-tax profit of £2 million was getting nearer to the Chairman's target of 15% return or £3 million pre-tax profit. There was still more that had to be done.

John had decided to close his O.G. and put away his pen in 1994, but he just couldn't as 1995 was going to prove momentous. In March Jane and Tim proudly announced the birth of their twins Benjamin and Joshua. Successors at last and John now hoped JSR Ltd would go on to the third generation. He never appeared to consider that girls could farm despite the fact that he had married someone from a non-farming background who quickly came to have an interest and valuable input to the farming company. He was very content to see that both of the new "Rymer entries" had Sykes as a second Christian name.

Carol and John celebrated ten years of marriage on the Isle of Skye which must have come as a total contrast to the warmth of the Seychelles they loved so much, but there was a reason for in May they followed the first delivery of JSR Healthbred gilts out to South Africa. Carol had not been back since her husband had died shortly after their return to England fourteen years earlier.

In November 1995 the Chairman's half year report for JSR Farms' shareholders, in effect his daughters and their husbands, forecast a profit after tax for the coming year of £2.1 million which was, for the first time, hitting his financial goal and he put down to particularly good trading conditions and not to any particular management expertise, for in that department there was still much to be done. He warned that any dividend would be kept to a minimum in order to keep reserves high. He pointed out that the Company may seem big to them but with a £15 million turnover it was really quite small. He was of course talking across the board for in farming terms JSR was in the top league.

He went on to forecast big changes over the next five years with emphasis on new management structures with divisional MD's backed by the new JSR Training Centre. He saw no substantial investment, especially into more land, but the contractual farming side he hoped would spread the farming company's overheads. In fact by the time he made his statement the contractual business had already taken over a 3,000 acre farm in North East Scotland, a departure from the original proposal to expand only over a maximum of 20 miles from an existing farm. He finished his report by saying that one investment that JSR Healthbred had to make would be in a secure nucleus breeding farm to cater for their growing market for breeding stock.

On Christmas Eve he closed the Omnium Gatherum and set off with Carol to a new island, Bonaire in the Dutch Antilles, but at sixty-four years of age he was concerned by the speed of change in I.T. He didn't explain why but he was confused by its application and, I suspect, possible misapplication for in one of his final sentences he spoke again as the Mentor: "I look forward to standing back to watch the JSR Way go from strength to strength. Tim and his Board face many challenges, but I will be there to grab the tiller if they meet troubled waters".

Succession to his family, and that of Carol, was well planned and ensured that internal dissent could not hamper the farming operations on the land. However what he could do nothing about was succession to the third generation of eighteen mutual grandchildren.

He closed thinking Tim would need to address all this in his turn around 2015 as the O.G.'s contents were passed down the family. He would then be 83. He looked forward to it.

8

1996

After returning from their New Year trip to the sun John knew all was not well with his health. In his sixty-four years he had never ailed apart from a back that was weary of sitting and travel constantly aggravated by the heavy work in the early years at Eastburn Warren. He had cancer. He was very brave and philosophical, conscious that it was now unlikely he would play that aged mentor role with Carol by his side, to pass the baton on to Tim in the way he had planned for some years.

He knew JSR was well staffed, but Tim was not quite there yet for he had planned another five years in his development programme, surely he could beat cancer? Mind over matter would do it. He had to win just one more time. He called non-executive Director John Davies to his bedside and asked him to hold the reins; temporarily of course.

In late July 1996 he died in hospital in Leeds.

Tim asked Giles Brand, Carol's son, to go with him to Leeds to bring John home to where he belonged. Before putting John into the car they enquired of the hospital the necessary conditions in which to place the body. A mobile call back to the farm ensured that the chilled potato store was set at the right temperature and a couple of hours later John Sykes Rymer was resting in the very heart of his creation.

The family agreed they wanted a very private service and burial. So it was that John was taken to Kirkburn Church in a walnut coffin made on the farm from a tree planked and donated by his neighbour, Robin Smyth and made by John Wilson who John had supported and encouraged to set up his joinery business. The coffin was bedecked in wild flowers picked that morning by the grandchildren from along the walkway that he and Carol had created. He was then taken back to Southburn and buried near the beloved confluence of the Southburn and Eastburn Becks.

Between coming home and being covered in the Wold soil he knew so well and loved so much the staff and most of their families came and said Goodbye in the potato store.

On August 16th 1996 over 1,000 people congregated in Beverley Minster and the Bishop of Hull in his address said, "John's success was in his leadership which in his case can be described as Followship. He had a following afar, he led many and his influence will go on. That is his legacy".

But of course that wasn't the end for farming stops for no man going on under the constant influence of Nature and worked only by man. John Rymer had worked his stone ground well.

9

The Way it Happened

I have described the way John's dream matured far exceeding his original 1,000 acres dream which, when he started, could never have been foreseen. Financial markets, a mix of food security and fluctuating demand along with a national cheap food policy conspired to give the market for land a constant lift. From £55/acre in 1957 it went up, with occasional dips, and in 2008 that same block of land at Eastburn Warren could well sell for over £4,000/acre.

The value of the pound has, of course, changed a lot over the fifty years but as populations rise, as fertility is squandered under concrete and human neglect one over-riding factor should be in people's minds for: "God don't make it no more."

The security of land ownership was the foundation of the man's success, his application of science to husbandry, his love of the soil as a precious asset and his training and leadership of men were the building blocks of the Company that exists today.

Each division of the Company is intricate, put them together and they become woven into a successful, sustainable land management system. What follows is, I hope, an easily understandable description of how it all happened.

10

The Fabric of the Farm

To many people large scale and profitable farming spell bad news for conservation and the rural environment which in the majority of cases is misleading. John Rymer was interested in nature as a very young boy starting to notice birds and insects in the garden of his family's Victorian house in Acomb during the first seven years of his life. Then in 1939 they moved to Bachelor Hill, still in Acomb, with a large garden and open country stretching away beyond.

With the help of friends and his brother David he created small landscape features in this new "world", gradually he roamed away through the rough country beyond to Acomb Bog and on into the mixed farming surrounded by the well kept hedges of Penty's farm. At prep school Wentworth Ping cultivated a love of nature, a curiosity about the how and why along with a concern for conservation.

At Greshams he roamed to the coast seeing, for the first time, the wealth of waders, sea and shore birds of the Norfolk Coast. He won a prize for his study of a stagnant pond and wrote an excellent report on the tundra country to be found in the Cairngorms. He was a naturalist long before he was a farmer.

During National Service he worked with dogs, he learning to achieve harmony between man and animal while his dogs learnt to sniff, detect and track military style. Later in life he applied this knowledge to gundog training.

At Cambridge he started to shoot which was possibly unusual for a boy who to date had no involvement with any of the field sports. In the '50's the upper/middle class public school community of the University had a "country gentry" culture in which shooting, fishing and hunting were very much part of the under graduates' lifestyle.

John opted for wildfowling having seen huge stocks of ducks and geese during his coastal trips from school and such was his interest in it that he accordingly started a wildfowling society. A sport of dawn and dusk, of stealth, patience and frequent damp discomfort mixed with convivial evenings. It suited his character for he liked to operate alone yet to be part of a team. Crouching in marshland in half light awaiting the calls of approaching geese, listening for shots from his companions, often a few hundred yards away, and then chilled and hungry meeting in an isolated pub to sit by a roaring fire before a steaming soup to comparing the sport — he enjoyed it.

At Burton Pidsea he decided that farming was for him, it was a way of bringing a practical and, hopefully, profitable bearing on his interest in and knowledge of things natural. City life had none of that. Tommy Harrison introduced John to the farmers shoot. Days after harvest when a group of neighbours and friends with a pack of labs and spaniels would meet to beat out the root crops and spinneys, walk the stubbles, lunch on good food and wine, return to the land in the afternoon and finishing off before a roaring fire, glass in hand, discussing the sport and the farming they had seen over the day.

Gradually as he got the bit between his teeth to farm 1,000 acres John's shooting days declined. There were more important affairs to be dealt with. He continued to shoot for when time allowed, but like so many the keenness diminished as the years went by, not in any way because of frailty and age but, one suspects, due to the repetitive nature of the sport.

His daughters went through the pony stage, but Father got little pleasure from such things as the Pony Club, which seemed to him, stuck in the days gone by with an out of date upper class atmosphere amongst which he felt uncomfortable. He never rode but saw hunting as a natural part of rural life. As a farmer he saw more disadvantages than the pleasures but, by and large, he allowed the Hunt on his land.

He did however spend some time with footpacks in the Cumbrian fells which he greatly enjoyed. The working hounds could nearly always be seen and heard going on and over the steep high fells. The followers did not have the upper class voices of the hunting world to the east and were always anxious to talk to all who were following. He wrote a poem about one visit which illustrates how footpacks were to him natural sport. He spent a day with the Blencathra Fell Hounds, John Peel's pack, in the company of the Deputy Prime Minister Willie Whitelaw meeting a lot of people, enjoying the 'craik' and ending the day dining with Joe Harris, the ebullient laird of Brekonborough near Penrith. Had he lived in the west he would certainly have done more of it, but he was an arable man from the east.

Fishing he did enjoy and he was well enough taught to be able to fish the good salmon beats in the North.   He was a riparian owner on both Eastburn and Southburn Becks, commonly known as the Driffield Beck at their confluence, a unique chalk stream in the North of England and well stocked with wild brown trout. He rarely fished those waters I suspect because being so near home, office and farm would have been too close, he would have felt guilty.

He starting farming in 1957, by 1969 he was farming 4,000 acres and in 1970 over 5,000 acres. It was the purchase of Southburn in 1974 that allowed him to renew his interest in conservation. He was well aware that modern farming could so easily be in direct conflict with the natural environment but when he started farming Government grants had encouraged the removal of hedges and small woodlands in the interests of increased food production. Field sizes had to become larger as tractors and implements became ever larger, but that was no excuse to neglect or remove all hedges, trees and woodlands which encourage the wildlife that is so important to maintain that all-important natural balance.

Insects, especially spiders, were mostly working in the farmer's interest consuming other invading species that may be carrying diseases or aphids with an appetite for growing crops. If birds and small mammals live on insects and worms, bigger birds eat lesser birds and all is well on the Wolds. Then of course there were rabbits, pigeons, crows and jackdaws each in their own way potential invaders of crops. None were a trouble if in balance.

In 1971 300 amenity trees were planted on tenanted land at Southburn when John was spurred into action having seen the destruction of Dutch Elm Disease over previous five years. He determined to get on and care for trees as he'd always intended. In 1972 a new hedge was planted using 2,000 quickthorns to split one large field in two and then over the next couple of years he planted 500 hardwood hedgerow trees so good for larger birds, especially hunting owls and raptors, as grandstands from which to spy for prey.

Stoneground

When he bought the Southburn Estate Hector joined the growing JSR workforce. In 1975 Hector and his small team started planting 5 acres of small copses, in all 85,000 trees. The mix: 38% European Larch and Norway Spruce as a fast growing cover crop and a main crop of 14% Sycamore and 10% Beech planted on a 10' square plan interspersed with the softwoods. There were no planting grants; environmental care was not by then on the Government's Countryside Agenda. The Estate Team proved a great success and over the next few years hedgerow and wetland trees were planted in great number.

In 1981 the Government suddenly became conscious of a need for trees encouraging policies already being followed by many landowners managing forestry programmes that had no hope of making money. They did it because they cared. By this time JSR Farms had planted over 100,000 trees.

Humberside County Council and MAFF introduced tree planting grants and Phase II Trees and Amenity on JSR Farms started. Experience had taught John that the 2 acre copse, or spinney, was an essential part of a healthy farm plan linked, where possible, by connecting hedgerow highways for small birds, insects and mammals.

Hector Robinson combined his role as gamekeeper with conservation and, as I write, he can celebrate fifty years working with the family. By then most hedges were maintained at a height of 9 feet with a V shaped profile making a good wildlife environment with height to lift coveys of wild coveys of grey partridge high over the guns. When John and Carol married in 1985 they planned the Southburn walkway alongside the chalkstream banks of the two becks. It wound around field margins, through woods and over open ditches and streams. The walkway ran a route from and to the gardens where an ambitious replanting scheme was underway.

Any wet areas were used as ponds and wetlands requiring considerable investment in dredging and landscaping. In January 1984 a gale struck blowing down spruce and the remaining dead elms left after the Dutch disease. Out on the farm every hedge now stood at around 9' with a metre wide base on either side from the centre of the hedge. Metre wide 'sanitation strips' ran besides each grass margin to keep noxious weeds away from arable ground. It is quite probable that the success of these margins in attracting small birds, grey partridges and hares contributed to the environmental requirements for 2 metre strips around all arable land introduced by DEFRA in the 1990's.

In his usual way John studied the history of forestry and in his O.G. he recorded many interesting facts. For instance in the days when our island was mostly forest there were only eight indigenous tree species: Oak, Lime, Ash, Wych Elm, Scots Pine, Juniper and Willow. All other species in our woods, coppices and hedges are introduced such as Beech, Sycamore and conifer softwoods. In Britain only 10% of the land mass is afforested whereas across the EU the figure is 30%. John had planted a few cricket bat willows which came to first felling in 1992 with 130 yielding £9,000 and two cricket bats of Southburn timber which were duly presented to Carol.

Britain now has 50 indigenous tree species and Southburn records show that 43 of these are present on JSR Farms, around the house and its policies. These are largely trees and plants suited to alkaline soils. The re-planning of the garden and the walkway were an opportunity to expand the plant lists with an another 75 non-indigenous plants and 25,000 bulbs including primroses and bluebells.

John's philosophical mind was constantly analysing and assessing legislation, modern attitudes and the spins of media and politicians. The Green Movement worried him for he maintained that history proves that farmers and landowners have been good environmental and conservationists over centuries with their records only being marred by legislation such as that between 1938 and 1970 when food production swamped sustainable husbandry practice.

When Humberside County Council introduced their forestry planting grants as the result of an environmental report that talked of returning to the natural environment which suggested to John that East Yorkshire had an unnatural environment, he asked, "Do these urban conservationists wish us to return to the 18th Century with open country and common grazing? The Wolds and Holderness must surely continue to respond to agricultural economics adjusting to modern demands for food and, in the future, fuel. If hedges are no longer needed then let trees take their place."

He believed National Parks and Areas of Outstanding Natural Beauty (AONB's) simply pickle areas inhibiting food production and stinting the rural economy. He also thought an important role of the 2% food producing population was to educate the other 98% to understand that applied botany and zoology sustain the rural environment while encouraging investment in a wider field of added value business.

When Nitrogen Sensitive Areas and Nitrogen Vulnerable Zones were introduced John saw them as precautionary measures created by scientists and legislators who refused to take sound agricultural science-based advice. To him the statuary 15% set-aside was simply knee-jerking against temporary surplus. Could we afford to have 15% of our productive land barren? Surely fuel production should be put in place on this apparently unwanted land. He agreed with sound scientific pollution legislation, but what, he asked, was being done about urban foxes, unwanted kittens, new age traveller camps, fly tipping and vast quantities of urban refuse. The lion roared quietly in his own haven.

The farm John Rymer created over his lifetime has shown the way forward for food and after his death for energy production, for that must be the primary function of all soil as populations expand beyond the world's natural carrying capacity. His farms were on very good land and sufficiently large to take advantage of scale, science and technology. East Yorkshire's climate is ideal as the soil has an abundant supply of sun and water, shortages are rare. The care of the land and of its fabric embracing the five foods that were produced right at the beginning and indeed still are produced twelve years after his leaving. This is his legacy.

The pigs fulfil their traditional role with their remarkable ability to consume most natural things to produce the most important meat that we have. Within JSR Farms they use cereals and straw producing pork, bacon and natural fertility to fuel the soil for the next crop. In the early days the small breeding herd lived outside consuming grass and clover in addition to cereals, but as scale increased and labour became more expensive buildings and mechanisation took over.

The potatoes were, and are still, the most valuable crop whether grown as seed, for direct use or for processing to chips, crisps and other convenience foods. In today's conditions irrigation, up-to-date mechanisation and storage are all essential and despite modern science still the minute potato eelworm prevents intensification. Grow the potato too frequently and the soil quickly plays host to this small pest that can then take years to get rid of.

Cereals, mainly wheat but also barley, are the staple of the farm taking about 50% (1652 hectares) of the croppable acreage producing in excess of 12,000 tonnes annually. This is the backing on which the fabric fits, acting as a break for potatoes, interacting with rape for both food and fuel, and peas – a crop that converts Nitrogen from the atmosphere to store in its root system for the benefit of the succeeding crop.

And then there is the grass, an inevitability on all but the rarest of farms such as those on the warp and fen soils. John was not a fan of grass as a commercial crop. In his early days he put great stead on short-term clover/grass leys that put Nitrogen and humus back into his ground, but as science and fertilisers improved he was able to replace these with crops such as rape and peas to fulfil a similar role. However on the Givendale farm there was a lot of grass and this made the bulk of the 384 hectares (840 acres) in the total acreage. This had to play its part in producing profit.

On-going genetic improvement has been the key of success in food production's record of keeping supply ahead of demand. John himself was a world leader in improving the pig with his genetics present on every continent. So it comes as no surprise that he hankered to do something with the ruminant; cows and sheep, as they could consume grasses and clover turning them into beef and lamb through their remarkable five stomach digestive system.

With his grass he was lucky in that early on he found Richard Fuller, a man of ruminants, who had learnt his farming in the wet climate of Wales where balanced grazing by the combined mouths of both cattle and sheep, working together, ensured a beautiful and productive landscape and good red meat.

John's interest and enthusiasm was infectious and from Richard's arrival in 1974 the quest began to improve cattle. From standard cross bred suckler cows to the French Charolais which were managed on a strict performance improvement regime which attracted two other herds to form a Company: A combination of the three pedigree Charolais herds Givendale, Limestone and Birdsall, namely GLB.

More is said in a later chapter of the cattle, so suffice to say at this stage that by following the genetic development line, JSR were ultimately led to the USA, to a hybrid strain with which a commercial link was formed that soon became international. Sadly this latter stage came after John's death for he would have been both pleased and proud of what Richard had achieved.

11

Genetics – The Mortar on the Bricks

John Rymer built his business on land, most of which he owned and on which he built a farm that produced food. Over the years the variety of food grown changed, but the original plan for a system based on pigs, peas and potatoes has persisted mixed into, by far the largest crop in acreage terms, cereals: Wheat and Barley. Rarely is there a farm without grass and in the case of JSR Farms around 800 acres of steep natural grassland at Givendale farm required ruminant animals capable of harvesting the herbage as milk and meat, a role well suited to the progressive herd of Stabiliser cows which are dealt with later.

Over the last fifty years sugar beet, onions and sheep have come and gone from the farms. Today Wheat, Barley, Rape, Peas and Potatoes are grown with Pork, Beef and breeding stock forming the livestock enterprises. These eight products are the bricks resting on the foundation of highly productive land with each held in place by the progressive genetics, this is the mortar that has been the strength of the business as it has grown.

In 1984, John was an enthusiastic member of the Hull Literary Society and he was invited to present a paper on the influence 17th Century scholars had on the great age of English literature in the 18th/19th Centuries. He had good reason to accept for he was extremely proud of the Rymer name about which he had undertaken considerable genealogical research exploring his own genetics.

Shortly after he left Sidney Sussex College he returned to dine, as was his right as a graduate, and in conversation with one of the Dons the name of a previous graduate came up, that of Thomas Rymer who was commissioned by Queen Mary in 1693 to produce the Foedera, a record of the Nation's lands and transactions. His brother David, while at Sidney Sussex, used this ancient record, which he likens to the Doomsday Book, as a reference in his geography studies.

Thomas came from Yafforth Hall, which is still lived in today, near

Northallerton in North Yorkshire. Whether or not there is a direct link is uncertain, but John's extensive research followed the trail through to the point when a family of that name took up residence in the City of York

In the 17th Century most of the population was rural and the majority of people farmed or worked in the forest. If John's researches are accurate his roots were both academic and political with Thomas's father having been a prominent Republican during the Civil War.

His first connection with both agriculture and York, if a rather strange one, was through Peter Rymer who in the early 19th Century dealt in night soil, the manure of the middle classes in the City, selling it to the farmers out in the fields to fertilise the vegetables that came back into the City markets. He was known as Dung Peter, he started a coal business and became a Freeman of the City aged thirty in 1811. Truly a rural entrepreneur.

Peter became a Tory and a follower of John Wesley's non-conformist religion. He was elected to the City Council in the Monk Ward in 1838 starting over 150 years of continuous civic connection with the City Council.

Peter had a son, Matthew, who married Ann Sykes and her name was adopted very much as a second name for sons of the future.

Matthew and Ann's youngest son was to be the great grandfather of John Sykes Rymer. This was Joseph who married into the Leetham family who had links to the famous Terry family in the City.

Joseph Rymer was a remarkable man who built a large and diverse business while establishing himself and his antecedents as substantial and influential citizens of the City. He too held the Monk Ward doing so for 52 years. He was a J.P., a member of the Company of Merchant Adventurers, of which he was Governor in 1900, as well as being Lord Mayor on four occasions. He served on the World Ecumenical Committee as a Methodist and was Knighted in 1901.

Joseph's third son, he had eight children, was John Rymer's grandfather John Leetham Rymer, lay preacher, coal merchant and again City Councillor for Monk Ward. An upright Christian Edwardian who was hard-working, sober and honest. Sheriff in 1925, Lord Mayor in 1928, Governor of the Merchant Adventurers and a strict teetotaller who introduced alcohol-free Civic Banquets but they didn't last after his reign.

John's father, Arthur, was the eldest son and he trained as an engineer, the first of the family to do so, eventually founding Bootham Engineers. He continued to have interests in other family companies and was a founding father of York University, first Chairman of York Festival Society, a City Councillor but for Clifton Ward and Sheriff in 1949.

In his seventy-first year he broke the family's long Wesleyan Methodist tradition by being confirmed into the Church of England by Archbishop of York Coggan in a private family ceremony. He was disillusioned by his church rejecting an invitation to form a unified communion of faiths.

In animal genetics the breeder considers both the sire (father's) and dam (mother's) lines. From John's sire line can be seen that devotion, honesty, a strong work and community ethic and entrepreneurship. On the dam line, the Triffits of York, come engineering and civic responsibility, but we have to go back to John's mother Mary Ella Triffit's grandmother Frances Lockwood to find a farming gene. The Lockwood family farmed at Flaxton near York and it was great uncle John of Harton Lodge who sowed in JSR an understanding of good traditional husbandry as well as the frugal life that, in those days, went with farm life.

While at the 'University of Burton Pidsea' John worked alongside Tommy Harrison helping to establish the Fishers cereal trials farm where new varieties from the plant geneticists were put to the test. In the Large White cross Saddleback gilts he saw the benefits of hybrid vigour which was yet further utilised by crossing them with the selectively bred imported Landrace boar.

As the Company celebrates its half century the pig division has its own dedicated team who are of world class. John would be proud.

12

The Pig

When John Rymer bought his first farm British agriculture was moving into a fifty year period of subsidy dependence, but his three mainstays of pigs, peas and potatoes received no Government support without which each of these three enterprises had to use science and technology to the maximum and genetics was the most important tool they had.

Pig breeding in 1954 had changed little since Robert Bakewell in the 18th Century had advocated controlled breeding that only used the best animals. Looking back he was a visionary for it was 100 years before Charles Darwin suggested the process of inheritance in his "Origin of the Species".

The strategy of the pedigree breeder has always been based on the putting of the best to the best to produce better based on the 'eye' of the breeder striving to maintain breed type. John's first pigs lived outside and were Saddlebacks and Large Whites which were quickly joined by Danish Landrace. He was surrounded by other pig breeders and, in their eyes, had the temerity to start crossing breeds which was considered heresy, but he set the pattern that soon all producers were to adopt by breeding F1 gilts or cross-breds of the first generation.

Since those early days things have moved on a long way and those old breeders would never recognise the complexity of breeding programmes today.

There were some key moments in this great change and the first came in the 1970's when it was recognised that the criteria used for breeding sows and boars needed to differ. A sow needed to be prolific, milky and fertile whereas the progeny needed to be lean and meaty fast growers so to satisfy the market maternal and sire lines were developed separately.

Next came statistics and computers. Dr Henderson, a statistician, developed Hendersons Mixed Model Equation which was a method of distinguishing variations in animal performance between environment, the fixed factors of such things as males and females growing at differing rates and finally identifying the contribution of breeding or genetics. This eventually led to progressive breeders being able to analyse their different crossing programmes. However this was at a time of slide rule calculations and it was only when the computer arrived in the 1980's that these complex calculations could be carried out at great speed and so BLUP came into being in the animal breeding world. Best Linear Unbiased Predictions moved the pig industry forwards and John Rymer and his team were at the forefront.

Today JSR Genetics Ltd use BLUP to show the constant breeding progress of their entire herd which runs across continents. As DNA understanding increases so this too will be incorporated into the analytical process.

The scale of this type of work can best be illustrated by looking at the BLUP analysis of the UK Nucleus Herd which requires in excess of three million equations to be solved simultaneously. This is repeated in Russia, Spain, Argentina, Japan, Korea, Australia, New Zealand and Vietnam on a regular basis.

All of this work has enabled the Company to have five grandparent lines that form the basis of their breeding female sales. A 12X Landrace Composite, or hybrid, containing 25% White Duroc blood is the first then comes the 16X Large White composite also with 25% White Duroc. When crossed these produce the commercial gilts: Genepacker Gold X. The large white and landrace grandparents produce Genepacker 90 and Genepacker 120. Each of these is designed for specific management and marketing situations. There are four boar types each using similar breeding selection, the Duroc, Hampshire, Yorker and Titan are all trademarked as are the female lines.

Today JSR Genetics Ltd embraces three of the UK's leading genetic companies: JSR Healthbred, Newsham and Cotswold at one time their main competitor. They hold an annual conference for customers and co-operators from home and abroad who are addressed by world class speakers. In 2007 over 130 delegates examined the theme: Putting the Science into Practice. They looked back at the progress that had been made and then looked at the present day when 50% more pigs using

30% less food produce 33% more lean meat and 50% less manure per kilogram of lean produced. Artificial insemination and embryo technology keep moving forwards with ultasonics helping to improve meat quality all of which is now being reinforced by gene markers, DNA vaccination and RNA interference.

The Company is also involved in various joint ventures both at home and around the world and one of the most interesting concerns work with doctors at St James Hospital in Leeds. Here they are jointly working on achieving more pregnancies with IVF treatment, a good example of ways in which veterinarians are able to give a lead to medical science.

Through their research the Company has trademarked Prosperm Plus, a food supplement that maximises sperm quality in working boars to benefit both quality and quantity having a beneficial effect on little size and conception rates.

Pigs from their unsubsidised background have led the way in using science across the board to take animal production far beyond anything John could have imagined in 1952 when he was at Cambridge and it will continue. The question that has to be asked is how far will other species of crops and animals be able to develop as artificial support stops at a time when the human race is waking up to the fact that food resources are becoming over-stretched.

13

Peas, Potatoes, Onions and Other Things

When John started farming he created, what in later life became the JSR WAY. It developed over his farming life, but always adhered to the original 3 P's outlined by Tommy Harrison of the 'University of Burton Pidsea' during his lecture to the Agricultural Club at Cambridge in 1952. Whether it was on the Wolds or on Holderness the staple crop was always wheat supported as it was within the framework of Government support for cheap food production but woven into the rotation were three unsupported crops; pigs, peas and potatoes.

Originally peas were grown for canning or picking with harvesting technology as vining and rapid freezing producing still in their infancy. The year prior to buying Eastburn Warren a newly developed pea for vining was introduced by the Pea Growing Research Organisation near Peterborough. Genetics again moving food production forward.

Farm crops are all grown with the consumer in mind with quality as the target, but quality can mean many things. Taste, tenderness, visual appeal and price all come together in the final analysis, but for the farmer unless the gross value per acre of crop grown covers all production costs and leaves a profit that produces return on the capital invested in land, machinery and facilities then it is not worth planting. So if the best looking, tastiest and most tender pea cannot be priced to leave retail, wholesale and processing profit it will never reach the shelves.

The pea and potato acreages on JSR Farms eventually joined other growers to achieve a scale of production which allowed efficient mechanisation and 'in house' development while at the same time giving some control on the market taking the crop from the field a few steps closer to the consumer.

It was the onion that took the Company further down the integration road. The arable team learnt the necessary husbandry skills; the management had already researched the market potential and early crops proved a success. It was not long before a co-operative was formed quickly followed by a sophisticated processing plant. Markets were developed, even opening up exports, but eventually the onions were given up as the aim of the arable team was to simplify and specialise. The processing company was sold off. Proving as so often is the case in farming that a good novel idea immediately becomes copied by others resulting in over-production and a fall in crop or stock values.

As we move into the 21st Century with the problems over food supplies and security there will be many new opportunities for the farms. Rape, miscanthus, sunflowers and willow are just a few of the new crops that will be seen on farms in the future. Looking back 25 years in 2008 cropping reflects tremendous change. More wheat is being grown and less barley. Oilseed rape doubled in acreage, but it is now autumn not spring sown. Vining peas are less and no drying peas are grown. All potatoes are maincrop with earlies now a crop of the past. There is no longer Sugar Beet as the York factory had to close due to EU sugar policy. And during that 25 years Onions came and went.

Also the great quest to extend the acreage managed by JSR Farms on a contractual basis at the time John died was reduced because the costs of movement of managers and machines became just another complication at a time when Company policy needed to streamline the core business.

JSR Genetics and JSR Farms East Yorkshire are that core, coming up on the inside is the Stabiliser Cattle Company which has received Government support to grow its production and is now at the stage where a market can be developed for its beef.

14

Ruminants

In 1974 the Garrowby Estate offered John Rymer the tenancy of 998 acres at Givendale, a farm right on the Wold edge land that drops away down into the Vale of York. Now this was not entirely JSR's type of farming with its 400 acres of permanent grass.

The Yorkshire Wolds are very similar to the downlands of the south of England with good chalk/lime soils and their rolling surface wrinkled with dales or downs of natural grassland. This was foreign territory in need of ruminant stock with the ability to convert herbage to both meat and milk. None of the JSR team was enthusiastic about cattle and sheep and so it was that Richard Fuller, having been tipped off that a stock manager was required, knocked on the office door at Eastburn Warren.

As a result Richard was taken on as Farm Manager for the Givendale Farm working with Malcolm Pearson who had retained his interest in beef and sheep from his days in Beverley as a Government agricultural advisor.

The farm was run down, the dale land under-grazed, thorn bushes encroached everywhere and the buildings were inadequate for any system that would meet the budgetary targets set back at H.Q. To start the new enterprise 800 crossbred ewes were taken over from the previous tenant along with his shepherd and a new herd of 150 Aberdeen Angus heifers out of Friesian dairy cows.

This was at the start of the Continental cattle revolution. British beef breeds had become too small and fat for the diet of a country becoming increasingly sedentary. However the dairy herd was changing and moving away from the quiet beefy Friesian cow, that had been responsible for supplying 80% of the nation's beef, to its slim Marilyn Monroe cousin, the Holstein. The result was a growing supply of meat lacking in both quality and quantity. Something had to be done.

In 1961 the Government agreed to allow beef breeding trials on dairy cows using French Charolais bulls through artificial insemination to see if these large, lean, fast-growing cattle would re-establish the beef potential of dairy herds. So successful was this that in 1971 the UK doors opened to a number of Controlled breeds, mostly from Europe, including Limousin, Simmental and Blonde D'Aquitaine, all of which took place under the strictest laws of quarantine.

Richard Fuller had mostly been involved in dairy farming up to that point of his career and was well aware of the way milk cows, through better breeding, had progressed from typical yields of 700 or 800 gallons to 1,500 – 2,000 gallons. When he joined JSR Farms he realised he had become part of a Company which applied similar principles to pig breeding, but with a difference, for they were not confining their work to one breed, instead they were using the 'magic' of hybrid vigour achieved by crossing two separate breeds to give a boost in the production of the resulting progeny.

Malcolm Pearson soon realised that he and John had employed just the person they needed, someone who could interpret their scientific approach to the non-ruminant in order to improve profitability and marketability of the ruminant. What they didn't know at the time was that he also had another side in his keen interest in natural history and photography which approached a professional level. The Wolds and Dales combined to give Richard a unique chance to bring farming, flora and fauna together on what was now 'his thousand acres' and be able to record the progress of changing the farm on film as a lasting record of change. John Rymer enjoyed his work and its results.

This was the only ruminant enterprise within JSR Farms which developed relatively slowly compared to the pigs where maturity came quicker, gestation was shorter and the results of management more easily predicted. Nevertheless today the cattle produced by the Company are leading radical change in UK pastoral beef production. The course of their development is interesting.

Using the Meat & Livestock Commission's technical service of progressive breeding in the beef and sheep industry, which was still reluctant to move away from tradition with breeding based on the show ring, Richard bought a Charolais bull from the Grove Herd and the progeny performance results were compared with other bulls being used in the herd. This proved that selection based on an animal's own performance lifted profitability in the resulting progeny. In fact that particular bull raised the herd's beef yield by seven-and-a-half tons, a very substantial and profitable improvement.

Richard went back to the Grove Herd to buy a cow with a bull calf at foot and she, Ailsa, with her son Olympus, created the Givendale Herd of pedigree Charolais cattle.

In 1986 Richard won the MLC Grass to Beef Award and in the same year produced his popular book on progressive suckler beef production. Olympus semen was being marketed into the dairy herds through the co-operative group Deeside Dairy Farmers in Cheshire and the resultant calves returning to a rearing/finishing unit on JSR's Haywold Farm.

The Givendale Herd, working with MLC, was the first to introduce BLUP breeding programmes enabling participating herds to compare performance across the country in a way that illuminated variations in management and environment. Best Linear Unbiased Profiling has since become standard in progressive breeding programmes.

By 1990 all of the breeding bulls produced at Givendale were sold direct to breeders without reference to show results, the traditional benchmark amongst pedigree breeders. Showing was previously regarded as an essential and costly business which has been gradually eroded away over the years, but in some cases it is still seen as the most important criteria in breeding selection. The GLB Beef Group was eventually formed bringing together three Charolais herds each committed to performance recording using BLUP. Progressive commercial suckler breeders wanted their bulls. So the names of the Givendale, Limestone and Birdsall Charolais herds came together with 100 breeding cows with potential bull sales for 40 – 50 per year. The BLG Group expanded to over 300 cows in 2002, but by then very many herds across all breeds were using BLUP and the bull market was becoming over supplied.

In 1996 BSE hit the cattle industry very hard, subsidies were clearly going to be withdrawn at some unknown date in the future and beef production at Givendale was facing long term problems of profitability. There was another problem in that the suckler cows to which GLB bulls were mated were largely based on 50% Holstein blood which was a ridiculous handicap to any farmer trying to convert losses to profit.

It appeared to Richard that nobody was doing much about the nurse cow problem. He looked around the cattle business. Dennis Cadzow and his brothers had stabilised the traditional Highland and Shorthorn cross thus avoiding the need for continual crossing to supply the Kylo cross heifer to tough farms in the Highlands, on the Western Isles and further afield in upland Britain, but that was all. He concluded that apart from the Cadzow family no-one else appeared to be addressing the problem.

In 1995 Richard attended the influential Cambridge Cattle Conference and was interested in a paper by an American, Lee Leachman, who explained how he and his family had set about a crossing programme to lift the quality of ranch bred cattle, the source of US beef to enter the grain feeding lots.

In the following year, the BSE year, Richard shared the platform at the Malvern meeting of the British Grassland Society with Lee Leachman and this opened the next door, one that led up a fascinating path which he took with conviction.

Pedigree breed improvement, artificial insemination and sexed semen each conspired to further limit the demand for bulls. Beef output in Britain was dropping under the increasing Holstein influence so if quality beef was to be produced it would have to be from grazing suckler cows. The big question was what cows?

In Spring 1997 Richard Fuller, Tim Rymer, Robert Rook and Nick Baker, the latter two being neighbouring farmers with suckler herds, travelled to the Leachman ranch in Montana and were impressed with what they saw. Tough, compact, milky, hard working cows with tremendous calves running with them at the end of the harsh Montana winter.

Back home a plan was hatched. Leachman was already developing his thinking on the utilisation of hybrid vigour from red bovine genetics. Hybrid vigour, that unique improvement in performance achieved when two pure breeds combine. The red genes he was using came from Red Angus, South Devon, Hereford and Gelbveigh cattle.

In 1997 the GLB group changed its direction, and name, to the Beef Improvement Group an organisation with the resources to produce the very best Charolais bulls and now, if they followed the Leachman line, they would be able to produce the Stabiliser suckler beef cow to meet the demands for beef production from pastoral agriculture. In November Richard was back in the US gathering embryos from Stabiliser cows to place in a batch of heifers that were ready and waiting at Givendale to allow the first steps to be taken down a path that could have a huge effect on profitability. From that initial 100 eggs a 53% pregnancy rate was achieved. They were on the brink of having Leachman nurse cows' on the ground in the UK for the first time. The Stabiliser had arrived.

Next a group of twenty farmers interested in working with BIG were taken to the USA, all returned impressed and committed. This came at the time DEFRA introduced the Agricultural Development Scheme and with the help of a funding consultant the Stabiliser Cattle Company applied for this Government assistance to expand this potentially valuable programme which could probably make pastoral beef production sustainable bringing about both economic change and a lift in the quality of beef entering the meat chain.

Eventually this application helped three regions to establish Stabiliser centres: Givendale, North Wales with Aberystwyth University and North Lancs/South Cumbria. Today the Stabiliser Calf Company has a database of 25,000 cattle and is growing 30% year on year. 9,000 cows are crossed to the Stabiliser annually and so far 2,500 embryos have been transferred.

Richard Fuller has achieved a tremendous amount in the last ten years and the point he is always keen to make is that the Stabiliser is not simply a cross bred cow. The Clay Centre in the USA, working with Leachman, spent a lot of time unravelling the subject of hybrid vigour and in this way arrived at the four breed mix run under the very tight control of a computer programme that prevents either in-breeding or line breeding occurring which, if it did, would then destroy the inherent performance improvements would be lost.

It would be wrong not to credit Richard also with his remarkable skill as a wildlife photographer. While his son, Robert, is now one of the

Stoneground

UK's most notable wildlife artists Richard produces wildlife studies that are acknowledged as being amongst the best.

To John Rymer Givendale was something apart from the rest of his empire. Richard Fuller himself was different from the rest of his executive team and the farm had that mix of permanent grass with trees, ponds and extraordinary wildlife. Above all what, back in 1974, had seemed a nuisance, grass, had now become a forward thinking red meat production possibility.

John, especially with Carol by his side, loved to go to Givendale, he was proud of the recognition that Richard received for his conservation work. Without doubt the Founder would have been very satisfied today to see an emerging beef production chain developing; Givendale Prime Beef, backed by a supply chain currently at 3,000 steers per year and expanding at 30% annually which is expected to double to 6,000 by 2010.

15

The Population Bang

From the early 1960's John was aware of Global Change as it would effect food supplies in the future. Few farmers, or their leaders, gave little thought over the years to this emerging and potentially devastating problem. The award of a Churchill Scholarship in 1975 gave John a chance to look at two of the world's sleeping giants, China and Russia. Both were vast territories with soils from good to poor, rain in excess through to drought with climate extremes of every sort apart from tropical. Both were emerging from social, political and economic chaos but it was evident that there were people in both countries who were aware that food production must increase dramatically as populations increased and lifestyles improved.

Shortly before he died he added the following to his Omnium Gatherum: "One third of world crops are lost to pests and disease annually while the population grows by 200,000 daily. Technology must be constantly improved to protect crops using compounds that degrade quickly back to their base organic constituents and while we must strive to eliminate harmful insects and bacteria other beneficial creatures must not be affected, in fact we must always strive to balance ecology and economics." That could have been his lifelong Mission Statement.

As Chairman of Fishers Seeds John was always constantly interested in improving plant genetics, especially in Wheats. Through the livestock division of JSR Farms he took his place amongst the Greats in genetic advancement in farm animals. Robert Bakewell in the 18th C, along with people such as the Colling brothers, found that by selecting the best for your purpose and mating it with another animal of similar quality improvements were usually achieved. In those days however the criteria were very different from today.

In the 18th Century the expanding population were applying muscle and might to building the greatest manufacturing nation on Earth and they needed energy and this came from animal fat. Bakewell's sheep and cattle were selected to yield an energy source first and foremost. As dairy breeds started to be developed and improved using the many local varieties of cattle, fat content in the milk was once more the aim.

In Victorian times animal breeding became fashionable and much of the selection moved away from functionality to a style of conformation that had eye appeal which did little for food production, but a lot for the egos of the industrial rich who started to take an interest in land, farming, livestock and the showing thereof. Only thoroughbred horses, hounds and sheep dogs are free from showing and the human interference that goes with it.

As John Rymer was progressing from his original Saddleback cross Large White pigs towards a breeding programme based on selection for a market and economic specification there were other livestock improvers at work.

In the world of poultry vertical integration of the roaming fowl had created modern day broiler production with animal feed companies sponsoring extensive breeding improvement programmes which achieved unbelievable progress in a matter of a few years. So too with the laying hen as it was moved indoors, first to deep litter housing then rapidly on to the battery cage. In Yorkshire Cyril Thornber was a leader in genetic progression of hens. So convinced was he of the power of genetics in animal production that he bought the Colbred Sheep, a hybridisation programme developed by Oscar Colborn in Gloucestershire, the man who also took the horns off Hereford Cattle. Thornber's aim was to breed fast growing lambs with lean carcasses that were better than the existing animals which were mostly pure bred with which he could build a lamb marketing company. He was dealing with ruminants and variable land and management systems, it took time he didn't have and he failed. Scotsman Dennis Cadzow's family had large land holdings on Scotland's west coast and they stabilised the traditional Beef Shorthorn X Highland crossbred cows, which traditionally produced the Kyloe crossbred heifer and established the Luing breed which over the years has developed in many hill areas across upland Britain. I remember standing with Dennis looking at a large group of Luings on his farm on the Pentland Hills and remarking that he must be proud of what he had achieved. He replied, "Aye I am, but to tell the truth I need another lifetime to finish the job."

Another farmer, Henry Fell, just over the Humber from JSR Farms, created Meatlinc sheep for he had identified a problem in the UK sheep industry in the 1960's when Britain relied on a stratified sheep system that was producing cross bred ewes from hill breeds across the uplands. These ewes went down onto low ground to be mated to a variety of British 'down' breeds, or top crosses, thus producing prime lamb meat. Henry found fault in the entire system which was based on eye appeal and not on meat yield. In response he created a selectively bred top cross sire breed which is sold on a grid system related to forecast performance potential in the same way that the JSR breeding cattle and pigs are sold.

As John reached the end of his life Henry Fell was beginning to react to the negativity of Government to matters of food security and pressures on the global food chain. He brought together twenty leading food producers across the industry from dairying through cereals to vegetables and other crops. As a result the Commercial Farmers Group was formed in 2003 when the Department of Environment, Farming and Rural Affairs issued a statement containing the following ten word sentence: National Food Security is neither necessary not is it desirable."

The CFG responded aggressively; "Food supply chains are now stretched and growing more vulnerable daily. In Great Britain we need recognition that realistic levels of food security are both desirable, necessary and should be a fundamental plank of food, farming and economic policy.

They then produced the first of their excellent reports "The Case for Agriculture" in March 2003. The second "Pressures on the Global Food Chain" hit the desks of Members of Parliament, and others of influence, in 2004 as did "Ask Yourself These Questions" in 2006. The CFG members financed all of the research, publication and circulation of these hard hitting publications.

During the twelve years since John died farming has moved on tremendously. Who would have thought in 1996 that Eastern Europe would be moving ahead as fast as it is with farmers from around the world operating on these fertile soils that have stood unexploited for so many years? While John encouraged Richard Fuller to follow through genetic improvement in cattle would he have envisaged so much DEFRA support being given to the project? Would he have foreseen an emerging beef market inspired by Stabiliser cattle which was something he had hardly achieved with the pigs?

In the past decade the thing that has changed most is an awareness of the food security the CFG highlighted as on our TV screens we see graphic pictures of famine and natural disasters constantly increasing due to climate change, disruptive politics and economic mismanagement.

The CGF suggested in their latest publication that we reflect on a statement from the Department for International Development. "Hunger sows the seeds of conflict. Scarcity of food, water and fertile land leads on to environmental damage, poverty, conflict and mass migration. Improved agriculture is both powerful and effective in promoting peace. When food is in plenty hunger ceases to drive conflict and civil unrest."

In 2008 the JSR Farms are one of many farming and food groups across Europe that have achieved considerable scale of operations while across much of Europe and, to a lesser extent in the UK, many smaller farms will cease to exist as economic pressures increase. Indeed it is forecast in the UK that around 40%, mainly small family farms, will go over the next four or five years as direct farm support comes to an end.

John knew full well what was to come, although he had not set about meeting the challenges at JSR Management Policy level before he became ill. However he had put all the bricks in place in addition to a training programme intended to draw young people into the higher echelons of the Company, with genetic technology targeted specifically at world and consumer markets and a proven arable cropping programme. Since then the limitations of oil supplies, their territorial ownership, the consequential reduction in inorganic fertilisers, global warming, carbon footprints and the quest for sustainability and renewable energy all combine to offer both threats and opportunities to the farming business.

As the UK self-sufficiency in indigenous food drops towards 65% is it right that EU policy is set on unwinding rather than recharging food production?

JSR Farms on good land with the right climate and rainfall may well be beneficiaries on the world market in the future for they farm in one of the prime places globally. The question has to be can we afford to allow pastoral farming to go into decline when the ruminant industry, on which much of it depends, provides food and a managed landscape supporting tourism, lifestyles and wildlife?

Cereals, fruit, vegetables and a variety of energy crops can be grown on an industrial scale from which may come by-products that can be processed by the ruminants in the winter months when grass is not growing. By their constant grazing cattle and sheep maintain the uplands which constitute a large proportion of the EU land mass. Those same animals produce fertility, which will be of increasing value as oil-based fertilisers run out, by consuming protein crops grown in arable rotations. These crops will be ensiled as feeds, they will store free Nitrogen and combined with straw supply cheap feeds for cattle coming down from the uplands for their winter keep.

It would be so easy to see this as a promotion for organic farming, it is not. John Rymer had it all in perspective. When he died GM was only just being talked of, but he was already on the case knowing that there would be an ever increasing need for yields to increase knowing full well that no longer would chemical fertiliser alone be the answer. Throughout his farming life he never forgot the very basis of Tommy Harrison's talk to the Cambridge University Agricultural Society in 1953 which was about balance, about working as much as possible with Nature from which some things come for free. Nitrogen from the pea crop, the pigs converted straw and feed to fertiliser and back in those far off days clover leys too gave good grazing that built fertility on the precious Wold soil.

16

John's People

John Rymer was not a 'people person' in that he didn't seek to build a social circle; he was not clubby although a keen sense of tradition and civic responsibility made him a key liveryman in the York Merchant Adventurers. However he did identify with influence in certain people he encountered over his sixty-four years.

Probably the first man of influence was Prep School headmaster Wentworth Ping who had been left for dead as an infantryman in a hospital garden having been severely gassed. He regained consciousness as he heard the trilling of a blackbird in the branches above. He instilled in young Rymer a love of nature mixed with chemistry as a result of which he became committed to natural science. Ping was the man who sowed the seeds of farming, but with a definite emphasis on a scientific approach which was far from typical of the time.

Then came David Wallace, economics tutor at Cambridge, it was he who pushed our man from being the budding farmer applying his knowledge of natural science to embrace the new techniques of business management which hitherto had not been part of the average farmers' skills. The Royal Agricultural Society's motto 'Practice With Science' took on an additional word 'Business Practice With Science' in John's mind.

In his last year at Cambridge John was Secretary of the Agricultural Society and having been fascinated by an article in the Farmers Weekly he invited the farmer concerned, Tom Harrison, to speak. In John's own words, "This was an exciting evening with an account of a profitable business offering opportunities for investment and expansion". The three P's of Pigs, Peas and Potatoes so much at the heart of Tom's business success, became the keys to the future for JSR Farms. He also said, "Cambridge taught me to think, the University of Burton Pidsea motivated, kindled ambition and brought me out of myself for the first time".

A neighbour of Tom's in the village was Doyen Insurance broker Kenneth Hibbert who secured the first mortgage for £7,000 on

John's People

Eastburn Warren, who later collected the keys to the house and accompanied the new buyer on his first opening of the farmhouse door. Kenneth became a lifelong friend and it was he, along with Tom Harrison, who brought out the 'other side' of John; his interest in finer things such as philosophy, poetry, literature and art.

This poem "The Auguries of Innocence" from the political works of William Blake was read by John on the occasion of the marriage of Kenneth Hibbert and Kathleen Firth at the Unitarian Church, Hull on 22nd April 1978:

To see a World in a grain of sand,
And a Heaven in a wild flower,
Hold Infinity in the palm of your hand,
And Eternity in an hour.

Every night and every morn,
Some to misery are born,
Every morn and every night,
Some are born to sweet delight
Some are born to endless night.
Joy and woe are woven fine
A clothing for the soul divine
Under every grief and pine
Runs a joy with silken twine
It is right it should be so
Man was made for joy and woe
And when this we rightly know
Safely through the world we go.

So it was a team of Ping, Wallace, Harrison and Hibbert who influenced the Founder's development; each of them was considered a good and trusted friend.

Once that first farm was bought most of 'John's people,' apart from family, appear to have been part of the farm for despite his work on a variety of agricultural committees and panels, as well as his civic role in York, John didn't seem to have time for many close friendships. He did though have a lot of friends through normal family and local circles regularly entertaining and being entertained over supper parties and tennis.

After six months at Eastburn Warren John was familiar with his land and the men he'd taken on, but he needed a foreman for without one he would be tied to the farm week in, week out, limiting his ambition to farm 1,000 acres – one day. In October 1957 Harold and Clara MacMillan joined John as farm foreman and general helping hand staying with him for 32 years to the time Harold retired in 1989. He went from Eastburn Warren to manage Southburn, then Decoy Farms handing each over, in due course, to younger men. He finally took on the heavy land of Church Farm, Skerne, 540 acres bought in 1984 for £1,300/acre eventually handing the tiller to Tim.

Such were the true rural folk of those days that most of the wives played their part too. This was still labour intensive farming and the women were recruited to pick spuds, knock beet, roll fleeces, but in Clara Macmillan's case she helped Margaret in the house, had five children herself alongside the five Rymers and loved to 'get out'. It was Clara and her band of local ladies who took on the first tree planting projects at Eastburn and Southburn.

In September 1963 a JSR Farms advert in the Driffield Times for a farm foreman for 180 rented acres at Huggate brought Norman Wood into John's life. Within 6 years Norman was looking after over 2,000 acres which neither master nor man would have ever perceived possible five years previously. Norman fascinated John with his natural feel for good husbandry and, as they became friends, the benefits and potential from training men like Norman to greater heights added a fourth P to Pigs, Peas and Potatoes - People. They were the cement that made the structure sound. Norman was a simple hard-working husbandman when he arrived, capable of doing the best for crops or stock. His outstanding feature was his intelligence, his ability to look and learn, to grasp and master new technology. Like so many of his time, men and women, given the chance of a full education he would have achieved success in most walks of life. As it was he ran a large acreage and the central feed mill with five transport units. To him holidays were of no interest, he was a keen shot and amateur gamekeeper who regarded time away from his Haywold base as wasted time.

Norman was a big man in every way, he and JSR had a huge mutual respect and frequently when a new venture was in the offing the two of them slipped away to consider, together, the buying of a farm or the possibility of taking over a management/contract as far away as Aberdeenshire.

Norman Wood and Harold MacMillan both wrote movingly about their lives with John in the Group Magazine after his death. In 2002 Norman died, his heart was embedded in Wold soil for nearly 40 years and if it happens in that land far away he and the Guv'nor will be looking at growing opportunities, but they would have to be on the chalk.

Six years after Norman joined the team, by now the business was growing far faster than any of them could have anticipated, John approached a Ministry of Agriculture advisor from the Beverley office in 1969 to come on board. This was Malcolm Pearson, who agreed to join the Company as Livestock Director effectively putting him in control of the expanding pig business. Malcolm was loyal to the cause and he moved right through the Company during the next 26 years, retiring at sixty in January 1995. In his last year at Southburn he dreaded retirement, but he moved into Driffield and found a new set of interests in Driffield Agricultural Society and with teaching at Bishop Burton College.

From the start the two men complemented each other, but as the Company expanded there was no doubt they grew apart. Malcolm put great stead on tradition something John could always move on from. Sadly Malcolm was killed one day when out walking his dog in September 2001. Probably his saddest moment was when, as church warden at Kirkburn Church, he was the only non-family member at his old boss's funeral.

Over the summer of 1970 with the pig business growing steadily and with a huge acreage to farm John was considering how to strengthen the team. He had good managers on the farms, the pig staff seemed to cope efficiently and Malcolm Pearson was gradually moving into his role as Livestock Director. John was putting in an incredible amount of time on the farms with additional commitments at Fishers and his father's engineering company added to the committee work in which he was involved and it meant that office time was at a premium and financial control could so easily slip.

In October that year he appointed Peter Bradbury from Ernst & Whinney, accountants in Hull, as Commercial Director and including the role of Chief Accountant. Peter was with JSR for 13 years, a period that was none too easy in the farming business, making constant analysis of production costs and rationalisation which was paramount. Peter was an architect of change introducing new financial disciplines and sophisticated computer services. He liked being within a business, getting to know the people and introducing that all important business management into the farming business as David Wallace had instructed John 18 years previously at Cambridge.

Peter eventually returned to Ernst & Whinney, the JSR Company auditors, for 7 years and then in 1991 put up his own plate in Driffield. Auditing was transferred to him. His legacy when he left the Southburn HQ was the way in which he linked central management accounting to annual enterprise budgeting making the financial workings of the Company easily understood to everyone concerned.

There was one other thing Peter left when he went and that was Brian Richardson who came to JSR as a keen young commercial assistant to the Company Secretary Derryk Milburn. He was an early product of the Agricultural Training Board's leadership courses and precisely what HQ needed, a seed with potential which, when given the scope and opportunity, would grow, flourish and progress through the firm. Brian did just that and became Chief Executive from 1991 – 1995.

In 1995 the Group was divided into three divisions each with its Managing Director. In the process of change the pig division had to replace its M.D. and Brian moved in to pick up some very difficult pieces in what had now become a very complex international business. John decided to mothball the post of Chief Executive and add that mantle to his role as Chairman/Managing Director.

Once he had settled in his own mind that his life was to be about building a business in farming and food production back in 1957 he took his seat on the Board of Bootham Engineering the family firm, which signified reconciliation between father and son after some thirteen years. In those days industrial training was becoming recognised as being a part of building a successful company, apart of course from in farming.

Bootham's training advisors introduced the Kostick psychometric test at management level in 1976 and forty-four year old John submitted himself to an assessment in 'human resource management'. It analysed his leadership, work style, social and emotional nature concluding that he was: thoughtful, objective, self-critical and little interested in social involvement and without doubt he would set high standards in both himself and others, but he could not delegate and this was seen as an area of frustration amongst those who worked with him.

Through this exercise he became increasingly interested in the Agricultural Training Board which had been set up in 1966 and after ten years it was extending its interest to business management in farming and that attracted John.

In 1990 he once more submitted himself to personality profiling only this time it was computer generated and he was placed in "The Investigator" category. He saw this one as a defence of his shortcomings for where it identified that he was both stable and unflappable, liking routine, it identified his reserve, even shyness, with people and a tendency to over-react when things went wrong then becoming over critical.

This took place at the new ATB Management Centre amongst sixteen other Chief Executives of agricultural/horticultural businesses on a course run by another of John's important people, Ken Neilson. He came away determined to listen more to others and to try to appreciate other people's contributions to his Company. Subsequently he became Chairman of Humberside and Lincolnshire Training Board and a great friend and supporter of Ken.

He saw training as an extension of his mandate to JSR Farms to bring together a forward thinking team to whom he could hand over executive responsibility as he approached retirement and to lead on to the changes of the 21st Century.

It was in 1987 that John decided he wanted to work with young teams of people who could grow within the expanding JSR group. He wanted to rear his key managers and as a start the Board analysed job descriptions throughout the firm, but it took through to 1991 when an application was made for British Standard 5750, to receive official recognition of the success of the idea. From apprentices upwards annual appraisals with line managers became Company policy.

At the same time Total Quality Management (TQM) making the customer King was introduced, a commitment every employee had to make as part of the 5750 application, or as it was later known, ISO9002.

Brian Richardson became co-ordinator of the in-house training group which sprang up and took root; this was the investment in people who would produce pigs, peas and potatoes for the customer (consumer) King.

As part of this development John saw himself becoming, in his sixties, simply the Chairman working with three divisional M.D.'s following a clear and simple Mission Statement. All of this was recognised in 1993 when the JSR Group were awarded the Investors in People Award followed by the National Training Award, the only agricultural business to do so.

The judges were impressed by the Leadership Development Groups that put ten young people into a two year module which commenced with a four day leadership course in the Lake District. Tim played a big part in this and as the heir apparent it gave him the chance to identify talent early and nurture it for the future.

In 1995 John wrote in the in-house JSR magazine a congratulatory piece about the way the arable team had formed a construction team which, in the down time of winter, developed skills enabling them to take on large building projects. Such was the success of the JSR Training Centre that other companies took advantage of it.

In 1993 the senior management spent 24 hours under Ken Neilson's guidance looking at a five year business plan bearing in mind that the Founder would wish to stand back, just a bit anyway, in 1997 at aged sixty-five.

Probably one of the most telling moments occurred as a result for following on from it Tim presented his father with his own Counselling Profile which concluded that he was now ready to take over and it was then John realised he had to hand the baton on, but he had always been in charge, he had built the empire of which he was proud and he didn't want to hand over.

He appreciated Tim's view which was for him to pull back, but to still be there as the sober advisor. The five year plan of divisional restructuring, of simplifying systems, reinforcing training, all took shape, but as we now know he only saw the first three.

John's Family

Sally Shaw 27-1-59 married to a doctor in Queensland where they continue their involvement in a youth mission in Cambodia. Children: Matthew, Christopher and a little Cambodian daughter Polly.

Jane Newton 27-1-59 married to Rev. George, a vicar in Aldershot. Children: Sarah and Kate.

Timothy 18-11-63 now divorced from Jane. Children: Jessica, Lucy and twins Benjamin and Joshua. Tim now married to Zoe.

Belinda 16-3-65 divorced from David Sheppard, grain merchant in Lincolnshire. Children: Tessa, Anna and Polly.

Rebecca 19-1-71 married to David Overy-Owen, stockbroker in Suffolk. Children: Dominic and Melissa.

Carol's Family

Giles Brand 15-5-64 Solicitor in London married to Suzanne. Children: William and George.

Cathie 25-6-66 married to Nicholas Redgrove, Lloyds broker. Children: Molly and Chloe.

17

John the Traveller

John and his brother David first left England just three years after the war in 1948. Bootham Engineers was prospering, a sure sign being that their father had bought a gleaming new Austin Sheerline in which he took the family on a trip to Switzerland. So rare was this that cars were mostly carried across the Channel by British Air Ferries flying ex-RAF freighters out of Lympne airfield in Kent which had been a Spitfire base during the Battle of Britain. It was still using grass runways.

This was followed by family holidays in Normandy before leaving school and entering the army. After basic training and finding himself in the Vet Corps he was sent to Egypt crossing Europe by train from the Hook of Holland through the Alps to Trieste, in all a three day trip. There followed a boat trip down the Adriatic to Port Said.

His companions were three other conscripts from the Vet Corps all kitted out in pre-war cavalry rankers uniforms; riding pantaloons, putters, spurs and cheese cutter hats. Why the army resorted to pantomime kits is not explained. Across Europe there were members of all three services, from various nations and to a man they saw the quartet as remnants from some previous conflict, some sort of comedy act laid on to keep spirits high. This was probably the only time that John found himself being treated as a figure of fun.

Private Rymer, dog trainer, was stationed in Gineifa Camp beside the Great Bitter Lake through which the Suez Canal passes. Sand dunes stretched for miles, it was very hot and it seemed amazing that only five years previously Montgomery and Rommel did battle in the hellish climate.

After many months of dog training and sailing a three week leave was announced intended to allow conscripts to return home to their families but with the three to four day journey each way this meant only a week back in Britain, it seemed hardly worth it and so John and two friends went on tour of Cyprus spending six months pay saved by not drinking alcohol over their time in camp, journeying through Cairo and Luxor to reach the Mediterranean.

Cyprus was then all Greek, still very undeveloped and seemed very clean after the dust and chaos of North Africa. After a year in Egypt it was home once more this time travelling in an ancient troop ship. He was now bound for officer training at Eaton Hall near Chester which he passed consequently receiving a fast track to Cambridge.

Time at Cambridge was about academic work and hard physical graft in the long vacations on the Perownes' Norfolk farm. When he graduated to Burton Pidsea work on the farm took precedence, although a couple of skiing holidays were fitted into the busy life on Holderness.

Once married holidays became important as he saw little of wife or family such were the demands of the farm. Club Mediterranean fitted the bill perfectly with sun and sand, basic accommodation, good food and lots of activities for the family.

In 1967 John and Margaret with a group of friends, including Tommy Harrison, took a remote luxury villa some way south of Athens. There were servants who prepared wonderful Greek food accompanied by remarkable wine, a private motor launch for trips around the Greek Islands all of which awakened John's desire to know more of the ancient civilisation unfolding in front of them.

In 1973 he and Margaret went alone to the West Indies which for John aroused what was to be a lifelong love of blue sea, golden sand, waving palms and peace. It also brought back his liking for sailing so the next year, with the four eldest children he and Margaret joined a flotilla in the Greek Islands where at last he took the opportunity to read Homers Odyssey opening the mystery and wonder of classical life in time out of mind.

In 1981 John put two dreams together by taking Margaret to warm sea and sand in a last attempt to rescue their floundering marriage. He headed to the Windward Isles to join a sail training holiday in the light breezes and blue waters of the Caribbean learning for the first time how to navigate and handle a forty-footer. It didn't save his marriage, but he certainly learnt how to sail a big boat. He was fifty and the following year returned to the Windwards to celebrate alone, a quiet and very thoughtful time, but after few days he was joined by friends and they set sail together for two weeks and he took control. The first hurdle into his new life had been taken – he was back in control.

He didn't really sail much again after that preferring instead the safer, lazier options offered by the isolated desert islands he kept managing to find prior to their ruination by international leisure development which he hated so much.

When he first saw tropical islands in 1972 and read poetry by Gerald Manley Hopkins it inspired him to start putting words together and in his O.G. he reproduces two pieces of his work, Eden or Eldorado and What Became Of Man Friday which follows:

From Economic Imperialism to Rhythmic Independence

or

"What Became Of Man Friday"
"He was a comely handsome fellow, perfectly well made; with straight strong limbs, not too large; tall and well shap'd . . ." and had "a very good countenance, not a fierce and surely aspect."   DEFOE

Europe wanting all the time new wealth,
Columbus discovered first for Spain
a staging post in quest for Eldorado,
followed swiftly by adventurers;
aspirant new colonialists.

Whilst the gentle Arawak from a hammock
watched tobacco and sweet potato grow,
fierce Caribs travel from a world
of Inca and Azdec power soon
to be the Spanish main and settled
island kingdoms, "Caribbean archipelago."

Maritime prestige, great wealth to sieze

Top - Double cropping in China – John won a Churchill Travel Scholarship to study Agriculture in China and Russia in 1977
Bottom - Walking to work – there is no shortage of labour in China leading to an advantage in labour intensive cropping

Stoneground

Erosion on the Great Wall of China 1977

Top Left - In contrast to the Chinese approach, the Russians were organized into huge collective farms with enormous rusting, second-hand machinery and glued up by bureaucracy

Top Right - The Russians were more interested in rockets than food production

Bottom - Taichai – The Chinese demonstration farm that featured terraces carved into the hillsides to maximise irrigated cropped area

117

Stoneground

Top - John took Tim on his second trip to China and was impressed at how well the Chinese had improved their agricultural self sufficiency compared to the Russians

Bottom - Our men in Moscow. With Ashley Burgess and interpreter shortly after being arrested by the KGB for taking pictures of MIG fighter aircraft

Top - Tim in a pram with cousin Christopher Bryant at Eastburn in 1964
Bottom - John and Margaret with the family at Southburn House in 1972

Stoneground

Top Left - Camping holidays in Scotland were always fun not least because John never used designated camp sites. He would find a spot he liked and pitch the tent. Negotiations with unhappy farmers always ended well. One was a customer of Fisher Seeds and another agreed that the whole family could lead his hay crop back to farm as rent

Top Right - To guarantee quality time with their father Tim and Belinda needed to accompany him to the market

Bottom - With the support of other local families John and Margaret founded St Francis in Driffield. Tim and Belinda (pictured) were pupils

Top - Bonafacio – Corsica 1971 – the Rymer immigrants on another camping holiday in another nudist camp but fortunately dressed to go out
Bottom - Jane and Sally at Pony Club. John rarely attended these events

Stoneground

Top Left - Flotilla sailing around the Greek islands in 1980
Top Right - Sally, Tim, Beccy and Belinda at Penny Lows wedding
Bottom - Two families together, celebrating Carol's 50th birthday. Back row left to right – Jane, Belinda, Jane, Carol, Cathie and Beccy. Front row left to right – David, John, Tim and Giles

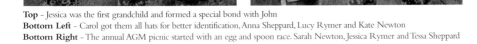

Top - Jessica was the first grandchild and formed a special bond with John
Bottom Left - Carol got them all hats for better identification, Anna Sheppard, Lucy Rymer and Kate Newton
Bottom Right - The annual AGM picnic started with an egg and spoon race. Sarah Newton, Jessica Rymer and Tessa Sheppard

Stoneground

Top - Molly and Chloe Redgrove with mother Cathie – Carols' daughter
Bottom Left - Christopher, Matthew and Polly Shaw at Ankram Wat in Thailand
Bootom Right - Polly Sheppard with Tasha

Top - There was never a dull moment when the grandchildren came. John would have some game up his sleeve
Middle - Dominic and Milly Overy-Owen enjoying the beach and surf
Bottom Left - Grandchildren just kept arriving and John started to resemble the Pied Piper
Bottom Right - George and William Brand enjoying a North Norfolk beach

Top - The first grandsons arrive – Ben and Josh
Bottom - The future of JSR is this way – no, it isn't, its this way

Molly and Arthur celebrate their Golden Wedding Anniversary

Stoneground

Top - JSR getting the measure of the local sow in Cambodia
Bottom - The Givendale, Birdsall and Limestone Charolais herds came together under the GLB umbrella to sell BLUP evaluated bulls and semen

Top - Due to the extreme Holstein influence from the dairy sector, Suckler cows were becoming too costly to manage. The removal of subsidies resulted in a different approach. A low cost easy care composite based on 20 years research and development at the Clay Centre, Nebraska. The Stabiliser had arrived closely followed by Givendale Prime Beef.
Bottom - The Genepacker 90 – one of the most prolific dam lines in the world

Top Left - The sire line Duroc was developed to improve meat quality in the pork supply chain
Top Right - The JSR Geneconverter 600 – a Pietrain Boar that became JSR's flagship product
Bottom - Tim Rymer who took over as Chairman of JSR in 1998

John the Traveller

by cannon and a cutlass. Carib Friday
turns to Crusoe whilst his brothers' lose
a fight for freedom. More Galleons and guns
arrive with Negro slaves exported
by triumphant tribal Chiefs in Africa.

Plant and work, for cotton, sugar cane,
spice and indigo. Find and tame
another humid island for the Queen.
Carry home exotic merchandise,
rum to blind the soul. Fill the chests
with the gold of others' labour,
satisfy the greed of old imperialists.

A riot and a hurricane, malaria,
new sovereinty, a plague of ants,
but the mill is turning profits
for a Greathouse with a French piano.
Nightfall with the sound of crickets,
frogs, the lights of glow worms in the trees
Rum cocktails on the terrace
and discuss the plan for cocoa, copra,
nutmeg and the price of mace.

Grenada spread her trade from
St George's Careenage
whilst Tobago's sugar crashed to ruin
in Gillespie's bankrupt hands.
Bligh's imported bread fruit,
green bananas and Indian mango,
Pomorosa, luscious fruit to tempt the birds,
Pidgeon peas and English spoken,
flamboyant tamarind,
Jacuranda, saman trees with
the stocking nests of yellow-tails

Stoneground

and many busy humming birds.
A diving pelican the scarlet ibis,
What does the tourist want.
He pays to see the reef or watch
the limbo and a modern
Calypsonian. Better listen
to the drums and eat the magic
of dead water bread baked outside
in ovens made of yellow clay.
Wonder at the calalu
or christophine and the smell
of wind and sea and watch
excited people dance a jig
and laugh and love themselves.

Beneath the lofty cocoa palms,
advisers try pangola grass.
The talk is oil and reconstruction,
politics and cricket. Independence
for a multi-racial prolateriat,
together bringing negro, indian,
creole, behind assertive mulatto
politician finding funds to give
their country ownership of vital
enterprises and cool black power
stirring trouble. Development and
tourism build up a poolside set.

"We are accustomed," but no longer,
times are changed, the lease is up
impetus to grab the reins of power.
A carnival of looting and rest
heralded their independence.
Now Raleigh comes to a marina,
not to caulk with pitch but offer aid

with new technology for industry
and food production. Hang up the cutlass
and co-operate in building packing plants.
Intensify and double crop, mechanise,
at last the world beyond will pay the price.

A transformed Friday, Crusoe's
noble savage finds he can command
and seeks redress too hastily.

J.S.R. May 1974

In both poems John's sadness at the collapse of such beautiful places is so well explained. I have a friend who was operating a game fishing boat around the islands John knew so well and talking to him I understand how they both saw this unique landscape, seascape and community simply fall apart in the interests of profits for developers who neither knew nor cared about these delicate environments.

1972 was very significant part of John's tropical dreams, although at the time he could not have realised it, for it was not only the year of his first visit to the tropical heaven with Margaret as it was only when he and Carol returned to Dennis in 1985, and she agreed to marry him, did he find out that she too had been in Mahe, the main island, at approximately the same time. Carol and her husband were returning to Hull having been working in South Africa and there they took a short stopover to prepare for their return to the English climate.

Once more a P, was inspired in the man to add to the pigs, peas, potatoes , people, poetry and philosophy. This time it was painting as a way of recording the wonders of diving down onto the continental shelf where large fish lurked, coral was radiant, plants swayed to the beat of the waves above and the water was so blue.

By the time 1994 arrived Carol and John had spent nine months living the dream and looking back it was the Island of Bird that proved their ideal haven with its 176 acres forty miles from the main island of Mahe with an air/sea temperature ranging only between 24°C - 27°C and constantly fanned by mild breezes. It was a far cry from the thousands of acres farmed at home, but sadly it was all about to change. In 1974 an airstrip was carved out while back in Mahe large jets were arriving with helicopters lifting tourists to every corner of this 17,500 square miles of Indian Ocean with its 100 islands of simple peace and tranquillity.

John Rymer, farmer, reckoned that to look at what was going on around the food producing world was important for before too long JSR Farms would be international players both as marketeers and producers in the world commodity market.

In 1975 he was awarded a Winston Churchill Travelling Scholarship to Russia and China as 'a muddy boot farmer' which, if the judges ever did believe it, he never really was. He spent a month in each looking at what happened down on their farms.

He took Margaret to China and animal feed manufacturer from Pickering, Ashley Burgess, to Russia. He found China the hardest to understand and returned again in 1977 with Tim to see more of the huge changes that were taking place. This was a time when both countries were highly secretive. In the case of China, the country was just emerging from the brutal dictatorship of Mao Tse-Tung who had died the previous year. In Britain the public had little idea of how they operated, what the country and its people looked like and this had resulted in total ignorance in the UK of the changes that were about to take place. Both countries were quite menacing, but not to John as he explored their history, culture and national personalities understanding the reasons for their recent violent past and the need for revolution.

To Rymer the mystery of Russian farming was that they had such a vast land resource compared to their population, but year on year they still relied on the plains of the US grain belt for their bread while the Chinese, with a population four times higher, was virtually self sufficient.

Not many people from the UK had been, or even wanted to go, beyond the urban and industrial centres of either country. Russia had 260 million people to feed all expecting higher living standards fifty years on from a revolution and two world wars. John saw himself, and Ashley Burgess, as informants to Britain about what was going on out on the Steppes. As he said, "If my study can help assess the potential increases in output and the objective of the current 25 year plan, it will have a bearing on world security". He proved to be right.

Here he was in the largest country in the world covering one sixth of the land mass with 75% of population lying to the west of the Urals and with half the land subject to permafrost, only 25% getting over 20 inches of rain annually and grain being grown on only 10% of the land mass. It was unbelievable both to the farmer and feed miller.

At the time of his visit Russia favoured industry and the production of mineral resources with agriculture getting second best both in education and investment. The peasant agriculture of the pre-Revolution era had been replaced by scale; vast collectives on excellent soils, equipped with poorly designed equipment handled by badly trained labour which was overseen by an army of statisticians, managers, scientists and professional services. It was not working.

He concluded after travelling 17,000 miles that at least ten years would elapse before food shortages would be overcome from their own resources. Looking specifically at pig production he saw a 5,300 sow unit which was fairly well run, but the final costs of the meat produced were astronomic due to over-manning by directors and vets.

In December 1975 he was in China with Margaret covering over 2,000 miles in 17 days; they returned dazed and incredulous having gone with very few pre-conceived ideas. It was so different from drab doctrinaire Russia, full of enthusiasm to overcome the chaos and crippled economy caused by Mao's Cultural Revolution.

They found the cultivated land well farmed with everything possible being recycled and at the point of the consumer the Chinese were such good cooks compared to the Russians. John was amused by the dominant pot bellied pigs which were everywhere in small groups consuming waste from the surrounding community, but he saw it as sustainability working on a wonderful level. He was impressed.

John likened China to a huge Victorian school working under very strict discipline with everyone in the same blue or grey tunics devoted to work. He thought that typical Chinese village life must have been rather like life in Tudor England. Clothes were simple, transport was by cycle, work was a six-day week and houses very sparse.

Stoneground

He returned in June 1977, but this time with Tim (13) and a group of agriculturalists. He could see the nation changing rapidly and concluded that the Chinese would become a major part of World Trade way ahead of Russia. The fact that the Russian population was comprised of so many races made a national identity hard to establish in an emerging country whereas in China there were close similarities across the country and a common culture.

Apart from these major adventures which were unconnected with his business John travelled extensively around the world building the JSR pig interests. I remember when Tim spoke at the Great North Meet in the early '90's he put up on the screen a map of the world with glowing points where JSR Healthbred pigs were and there in what appeared to be the middle of the Indian Ocean was a glowing point. "And what," asked a member of the audience, "is that?"

"Oh that's one of Dad's secret interests." The audience speculated never for one moment thinking this was a precious secretive tropical island retreat instead imagining confidential genetic research being carried out under the waving palms well away from the prying competition.

From the start of their lives together Carol was at her man's side on most of his business trips. Attractive, communicative, moving comfortably around any company whereas John didn't enjoy the social elements of working trips Carol oiled the wheels, handled introductions and shielded him when necessary.

He closed his record at Christmas 1995 flying off after the festivities to Bonaire, an island sixty miles off Venezuela, for the New Year 1996, the one he wouldn't see the end of. An island once covered in tropical forest now just one more emerging into tourism. They walked the warm beaches, dinghy sailed across lagoons and planned the future, but John was realising he was not well.

18

The Other Side of the Man

I was aware of John Rymer of JSR Farms from the time of my arrival in Yorkshire in the early '60's as he, and others, were riding the great wave of agricultural expansion and creating a lot of 'chat' amongst the rest of the farming community. Having now had the chance to delve into the true John Rymer I am amazed just how much he packed into his life. He explained his approach to life in his O.G. with this advice:- "Pack more life into your years not more years into your life". He certainly did.

He built his business with a great sense of succession and he enjoyed being acknowledged as a trend setter running a farming business that respected the raw material with which it worked, the earth.. He did not, as time went by, devote a lot of time to his family, nor did he to people outside his working life with a few notable exceptions. With Tim he had a very special working relationship that appears to have been a combination of paternal love, a pride in his progeny and a respect for his individuality.

He developed an interest in literature and philosophy which was dominated by the much enjoyed meetings of the Hull Literacy Society which from time to time demanded that he covered a lot of reading in order to present papers on nominated subjects to his fellow members. Around the time of his marriage break up he started painting and which became a mutual interest for both he and Carol. He also enjoyed poetry and enjoyed writing small aide memoirs in all manner of topics for inclusion in his archives. He was a prolific speaker and spending considerable thinking time in preparation. Five or six of his speeches are in his O.G. varying from hard farming business, blessing the plough, a eulogy at the funeral of his great friend, Kenneth Hibbert, and an address to the Women's Farming Union.

He was able to 'switch off' seeing it as a challenging diversion whether after dinner, in his office, when on long journeys or on those green islands ringed by white sand and tropical seas.

Stoneground

Sailing too was always a retreat and in the mid '70's he turned from dinghy sailing to much larger craft enjoying the challenges and control as well as the responsibility for others and the anticipation of the next port of call.

On these occasions he put words together describing, assessing and wondering as a form of relaxation and, I believe, it gave him a feeling of contentment in passing on his wisdom. Not only did he holiday abroad for he also travelled extensively expanding the genetics business and studying farming in other places, all of which is covered in a further chapter.

When he first visited the Seychelles in 1972 the coral reefs were unharmed, he dived and dived admiring them and yet when he returned on his 60th birthday they were dying. Dying under the pressure of people and this drove his thoughts on, on to the conflicts of population growth, the almost certain damage to the environment and, not least, to food supplies.

At 60 he was still playing tennis, around the year if possible, but he was not really a sportsman and saw the tennis supper or tea as a reason to be sociable and without which he may well have remained fairly isolated from friends away from his business. He smoked a pipe from his National Service days in Egypt through to the end of his life. He resisted the email, reckoned in 20% of his time he achieved 80% of the work he had to do and apart from a bad back and post lunch drowsiness he was fit as a fiddle.

At Cambridge he bought a shotgun and started shooting which he carried on for some years, but at 50 he stopped accepting invitations, but continued enjoying half a dozen excellent days with friends on his own land with his own wild birds. He hated the intensive rearing of pheasants and in later life enjoyed dog and gun and roaming in the gloaming, duck flighting on the clutch of pools he established around Southburn.

Of horses and hunting he respected the rights and traditions, but he did not like the attitudes and way of life of many who followed hounds. The girls went through the pony stage, but neither parent encouraged them to continue on from the Pony Club to hunting and other equestrian sports. From time to time the Hunt made a mess of a hedge or field edge on Rymer land which he did not appreciate.

19

50 Years

In July 2008 the JSR family with their staff and guests, will gather at the Southburn headquarters of the JSR Company to celebrate fifty years of remarkable progress since John took his first farm, Eastburn Warren, when he threshed the away-going crop of Bersee wheat into 18 stone sacks and carried them manually up the ancient worn stone granary steps to await the previous owner's collection and sale which signified that he was then really on the road and what a journey he faced.

To those of us who remember the countryside of 1958 the progress of agriculture seems remarkable. It was thirteen years on from WWII and a decade into the new era of farming and food production; the start of the Second Agricultural Revolution. The majority of farmers were only reluctantly moving out of their old ways while the likes of John Rymer, inspired by Tom Harrison a man ahead of his time, were taking advantage of the grants, subsidies and guaranteed prices that Government had put in place to ensure the British public were as near as possible self sufficient in food. The World War was over, the Cold War threatened.

In those days a walk from Eastburn due west across Haywold and Huggate to Givendale would have been very different from today. Over that nine miles men would have been at work at most times of the year, lots of them. The cropping, in much smaller fields, would have been more varied and there would have been livestock, especially large flocks of sheep, for those were the days before chemical fertilisers and sprays finally put paid to the rotational farming that had been the basis of good husbandry since the start of the First Revolution in the 18th Century. The crops would have been lighter on the ground with more underlying vegetation some good, some bad.

The cropping at Eastburn Warren in those early days was based on grass leys and clover to feed atmospheric nitrogen into the ground along with humus to maintain soil condition. Sheep ran on leys all summer and root crops over winter adding their contribution to the fertility of the ground.

Stoneground

On your walk you would have met craftsmen at work. You would see many a shepherd, the odd one with a horse and cart hauling fodder, moving sheep nets and preparing the lambing fold. Hedges, although never a main feature of Wold country, were being laid from November through to late February, the start of the lambing and land work season. Men with stout leather gloves, billhooks in hand, cut and laid the hedge while a boy, or old feller, raked and burnt the trash. In the natural cycle they would return to this hedge again in six or seven years to repeat the process, but as it turned out they didn't for labour was quickly replaced by the automatic hedge trimmer and hedges would never be the same again. In the background tractors without cabs would be noisily going about their business, driven by men wrapped in hessian bags for protection and when it rained with paper fertiliser sacks wrapped around their legs.

Apart from the business of farming this was an area of great estates and you would meet a keeper catching vermin, hanging them on gibbets for the approval of landowner and his agent. Woodmen were felling trees, extracting timber, sawing up the trash and replanting young trees. In September and October in the early morning you would meet the local hunt out cub hunting followed, from November to March, by fox hunting and the eternal conflict between gun and hound, farmer and sportsman.

Walk that way today and, depending on the season, you may well see no-one at all. You may hear nothing apart from in the air above and when silence does settle the sound of birdsong. But on a dry day in February you may hear the hum of a large self-propelled crop sprayer as it goes about its early protective role of crop protection. In July, August and September hubbub can break out over hundred acre blocks as corn harvest, baling, cultivation and re-sowing all take their part in yielding up one crop and preparing for the next.

Today every vehicle is quiet with air conditioned cabs connected to HQ by radio with stereo sound systems and well sprung seats that allow the man on board to work long days in ideal conditions. A long way from the man half a century ago who stopped for a chilly bite at 10am, warming his hands on the hot exhaust pipe, another break at 12 noon and 3pm before the long slow journey back to the farm at 5pm, frozen.

John Rymer, the son of the City of York, loved the Wolds. He liked to see himself as the archetypal working farmer yet had he been born one this book would never have been written. If on that trek to the west fifty years ago you had met him he wouldn't have been astride a tractor, he might well have been doing what was regarded as every farmer's best fertiliser; walking the fields, studying crops and soil condition and supervising the men at work.

In 1981 John opened a conference at York University for the Agricultural Section of the British Association for the Advancement of Science presenting an overview of the Wolds with 300,000 acres of exposed open fertile country, Britain's most northerly chalkland which had been farmed for 2,000 years. This was the year the Humber Bridge opened at last linking Lincolnshire and Yorkshire over the waterway that carried the vast flows of Trent, Ouse, Derwent and Ankholme. The audience were invited to get out and see the production that was taking place and to appreciate the importance of East Yorkshire in supplying the Nation's larder.

Brian Hebblewhite became part of JSR Farms when Southburn was purchased, he was a tractor driver with more than the normal attention to the soil he was working for he studied it as it moved over mould board or tine, like a hovering raptor, and occasionally he would stop, get off and retrieve a pottery shard or a piece of metal. In the early days when hoeing sugar beet he found quantities of artefacts all lovingly cleaned by he and his wife who attended regular archaeological classes in Driffield.

This was to form the Southburn Collection and heralded the start of the Southburn and District Archaeological Society. John probably surprised his audience by explaining how this apparently humble tractor man had such a huge sense of history as he ploughed, sowed, reaped and mowed, but in doing so he emphasised the difference between those who work the land and their counterparts in other industries. In fact the beneficiaries of this book, devoted to the life of John Rymer, will be those very people who across the countryside love and care for the Nation's most precious asset. The 50th Anniversary Pignic in July 2008 will include the opening of the Southburn Museum which will endorse the attention to much more than just production that John brought to his farming practices.

In concluding his opening speech to the British Association he referred to the Wold sheepwalks, enclosed during the 17th Century, which were regarded as the best wool and mutton producing area in Britain. In the 18th Century some Wold farmers still practiced nomadic cropping systems by ploughing out sweet grazing, taking two cereal crops, exhausting the fragile fertility and moving on leaving barren surfaces to slowly and naturally restore. His last words to the delegates were, "I hope you find time to see today's highly productive Wolds of which I am so proud."

Pride in his land came very much to a peak in August 1972. He was in partnership with Lord Halifax of the Garrowby Estate on the 1,997 acres of Haywold Farm. During the prestigious mid August York Race Week Her Majesty the Queen was a guest of His Lordship at Garrowby and on the morning of 16th August came a call to John from the Earl asking if he and his unnamed guest could come and look at the farm. John agreed as countryside gossip had already reached him about the Royal guest.

Margaret took Tim, Jane, Sally, Belinda and Mr Pepperpot, the family pony, up to the farm before the appointed hour and the ruse worked. The family, and the pony, met Queen Elizabeth II.

The Queen had come as a farmer wanting to see everything including the Fishers Seeds Company cereal trial plots where, in particular, Maris Huntsman wheat looked particularly well. To John's delight he was told it too was doing well on the Queen's Norfolk farm, Sandringham. She looked at seed potatoes, peas and met Norman Wood who gave an explanation of eighteen month Friesian beef production from grass. When Her Majesty drove away none of them could believe that the young woman they had just met was the same one that they had seen on the evening news the night before being presented to the dignitaries at the Knavesmire the previous day. She had inherited the genes of her kinsman, Farmer George.

When he was fourteen John was confirmed into the Church of England, the first conformist Rymer of York for a few hundred years. He had no great conviction and Methodism was one of the things he had escaped from when he left York for Greshams in 1946. In the Omnium Gatherum he dwelt a lot, almost in guilt, on Christianity repeating more than once that for him to 'love thy neighbour' was basically what he felt religion was all about. In the latter part he said that he went through "progressive conversion" becoming more humble, appreciating the gift of life and acknowledging the problems of the world. He hoped, as he aged, to be more honest with himself and thoughtful of others.

He read a lot analysing his depth of belief in Christianity he covered Ovid, Homer, the Bishop of Durham, C S Lewis and the researches of Ian Wilson in his book Jesus – The Evidence. He wasn't a great church goer, but to me having looked at the evidence I would say he believed in God, but was uncomfortable with a lot of his staff on Earth and the practices they represent Him through on Earth.

In 1996 on Plough Sunday he addressed the congregation of St Michaels Church at Garton in Holderness in which he mourned the fact that church leaders were expected to live on a pittance explaining why they are so often called incumbents expected, as they are, to attempt to balance the paltry church cash flow and carry much of the woe of the community on their shoulders. The contemporary changes in rural society with fewer farmers and workers, young people migrating to town and city and new folk arriving with no connection to that society had to be a challenge if the church was to survive in anything like its traditional role.

In this I believe he explained his faith, "Believing Jesus was unique and remains so today, putting science to one side and still feeling honest to God, finding Him more easily in my fields and country lanes and while communing with my day to day people." Perhaps after all he was a simple man?

During the first fifty years of the JSR way legislation increased yearly. Shortly after the first farm was bought, a decade before GB became European, the fact that small family, peasant, farms across the continent had to go, half a million of them, removing five million hectares from food production. This was a hard pill to swallow and it didn't quite happen like that, but the numbers of farmers eventually fell forced out by falling incomes. Today the land they cared for is once more being recognised as a vital food and power resource, but now under a different game plan which is largely following the JSR Way.

This set the tone of the legislators as far as farming was concerned. In 1965 the Home Grown Cereals Authority, supported by a levy paid by grain growers, was the first of a number of levy boards to be established. A year later the Agricultural Training Board, in which JSR became key players and beneficiaries, was introduced to move the traditional livelihood of farming into an industrial frame of mind. In 1967 the Central Council for Agricultural and Horticultural Co-operation emerged charged with inspiring and initiating corporate effort for small producers enabling them to emulate larger and more successful operators, it lasted only sixteen years before becoming Food from Britain to cover up its failure to get the message across. In 2008 the Labour Government's Department for the Environment, Farming and Rural Affairs finally laid FFB to rest. In 1967 came another levy board – the Meat and Livestock Commission set up under the Chairmanship of George Howard of Castle Howard, a near neighbour of the Rymer family. Another year on and the Countryside Act was introduced, the first indication that farming and food could lose their exclusive rights in the British countryside in favour of something the politicians suddenly called The Environment. Did they really know what this was or had they been taken over by the army of special interest groups that had gathered as food supplies met the national demand and wealth grew?

In 1971 the free National Agricultural Advisory Service which had been available to all farmers for twenty-five years was disbanded to be replaced by the Agricultural Development and Advisory Service, one more step on the road to industrial status, or was that the hope?

In 1973 the UK became European and after seven years of unease amongst farmers confused by the new, but not unexpected, regime farming came under the spell of the Common Agricultural Policy which quickly gave rise to the Wildlife and Countryside Act followed by the 1986 Agricultural Act both of which involved various non food producing aspects of farm land. In 2008 the merits of the WCA is being questioned as the press alert the public to the fact that the world really is going to run out of food and that UK food security is at an all time low. Set A Side has been abandoned, the RSPB complain that over twenty years of bird policies have been destroyed and another time of conflict between food production and 'other interests' comes into view. Left to its own devices farming would see to it that the countryside functions in the future in balance caring for all interests, but as we all know Government interference always puts things out of balance.

JSR Farms, with their care of hedges, creation of wood and pond with the huge task of reclaiming Givendale had great satisfaction in winning the Silver Lapwing Award presented by the CLA in 1995. This was for exemplary conservational management which John got a tremendous amount of pleasure and satisfaction from for his team had won this without giving way to its commitment to the production of good food.

In 1992 came the MacSharry Report announcing the de-coupling of production support for beef and sheep with a new emphasis on rural development, diversification and social support. In 2003 the Single Farm Payment Scheme was announced, the end of subsidisation becoming reality on May 1st 2005. The end of an era. The start of another.

20

2008 – 2020

The celebration at Southburn in early July will look back at the fifty years of progress achieved by John Rymer's Company and you have now read an account of it. By now you will appreciate that lying at the very root of his success has been a constant awareness of the need to balance Nature within fairly intensive farming.

You have also read of the clash between World fertility and the rising population which will become very clear in around 2025 as the food starts to run out which will coincide with ever-decreasing energy from subterranean carbon fuel in turn will create a shortage of much of the inorganic fertiliser that has driven food production for the past century.

John was a great philosopher. He looked back, often to ancient civilisations, but he also looked forwards. Tim does as well and now as Chairman of the Group he has his own thoughts on the future and he makes sure his Board is managing their divisions with an eye on the years ahead. After all as food becomes scarce and new sources of energy come into use agriculture will become the world's most important industry.

So as I finish this tribute to a great food producer what does his heir see in the years ahead?

Timothy Rymer sees the future in fairly simple terms unlike many people in the farming community who are uncertain about going on to the world market in 2012 as Government/EU support for production ceases. It is difficult for the typical farmer to feel he can be a positive player in what is clearly going to be a very different industry from the one we have all become used to for the past sixty years.

These rolling Wold acres will produce both food and energy in years to come. The closer the primary producer of food can get to the final consumer the more the profit is likely to be. Energy will be produced, but where it will go is at present uncertain.

Potatoes are the most valuable crop. The humble spud is taking on a much higher profile as increasing food production becomes a new priority with its yield of carbohydrates being one of the highest in arable farming. The cropping of JSR Healthbred Potatoes is split 30% seed, 45% crisping for Walkers with 25% being sold to the domestic market. Quality is the aim, but while the Wolds give excellent yields the minor damage to skins by the stone chips in the soil limits the quantity that go to the table market.

Peas are grown for Birds Eye and the 'own label' market through an agent. Once more the consumer is King wanting sweeter more tender peas which in the field means lower yields and so the grower works harder for less, but should he fail to meet the 'spec' and grow the varieties of old with their higher yields he will be selling a tough, large, bitter pea at below the cost of production.

The varieties of peas and potatoes improve all the time and are the product of plant geneticists, but with JSR Genetics the power is all "in house".

An example is the Hampshire line the Company has developed to produce high quality meat ideal for Cranswick Tenderloin Packs – a link much nearer the retail market, but the breed's stress levels needed to be reduced to reduce possible toughness in the final product. Working with a Scandanavian company JSR Genetics now have world rights to this high meat quality genetic package.

Pigs are the lynch pin to the farm policy with 75% of the wheat grown and all the barley straw going into the pig units. The wheat straw is chopped going back into the soil to maintain the humus level, so important in maintaining a friable fertile seed bed for the following crop. The manure from the pigs goes back to the rape crop.

The farms rotation, or its balance, stretches over six growing seasons during which deep ploughing occurs for three and minimum tillage (mintill) for the other three. Once more this is all about maintaining soil condition.

So what of energy? These rolling acres have a lot of potential and the Company has a specialist group looking at the various options available to them. Straw need not be chopped back into the soil, it can be processed into energy, but would that reduce fertility? If it were used in this way would one or even two years of a legume crop achieve the similar results? If it could, would the pea acreage expand or would clover, lupins or Lucerne be an alternative with their Nitrogen fixation talents adding to fertility for free from the atmosphere?

The rape seed can be crushed to provide either a domestic oil or fuel. Will the tractor fleet of the future be home powered? Is it a genuine possibility?

And then there is all that pig muck which currently is separated liquid from solid to avoid pollution risks. It is a valuable fertiliser, but it could go into a digester, produce methane gas and still have a fertile value after that. The power potential of methane is considerable either for internal use or for sale off farm.

There is also another possibility concerning Givendale and the Stabilisers. Tim admires the way Richard Fuller has linked Stabiliser Beef direct to a retail market by working with independent butchers and restaurateurs. This is an expanding market attracting excellent premiums. As breeding heifer sales increase, mostly onto all grass farms, so too do the number of cattle coming available for finishing.

JSR Arable Division could create finishing facilities for Stabiliser Beef that would almost certainly be capable of producing a kilo of saleable beef far more cheaply than could the breeder on the all grass farm.

So that may be the next step in the Stabiliser story. Contractual breeders or contractual finishing? Beef production processing wheat straw and consuming rations based on home grown proteins and cereals. All of which adds more home produced fertility to that all-important balance.

Over the years through land purchases and tenancies the Company has acquired 85 residential properties most of which are let on shorthold tenancies. As property values continue to rise Tim sees this as a division that could expand for in these days of increased mechanisation and technology in farming traditional farm steadings quickly become redundant. New facilities often need to be more centrally located leaving behind a site in need of redevelopment.

Many of us in farming today look back on the 'old days' of The Ministry of Agriculture, Fisheries and Food with fondness for the industry had a good working relationship with Government in those days; there were disagreements, but these were normally overcome without too much trouble. Since MAFF was destroyed to become DEFRA the JSR Company has found their pig division coming under more restrictive rules and regulations, particularly in relation to exports, their main market.

Such is the situation in 2008 that the Company is likely to move increasingly away from the EU, probably to Canada, for much of the genetic multiplication. In Canada every effort is made to encourage overseas trade from the regulatory level and protocols through to air freight costs.

The pig industry is now global. When John bought his first Danish Landrace boar it came to Garton Station by train. He met it, in its wooden crate on the platform, waited for the train to depart and then released it to walk it back to Eastburn Warren. As he slowly wandered behind the boar, which no doubt was hungry and stopped to eat as it went, I wonder what John would have said had he been told that in fifty years that pig's influence would have given rise to an enterprise of thousands? Then if he had dreamt that night of being forced by Government to take those thousands of pigs away across the Atlantic – it would have been a nightmare. And that is just what it is becoming today.

John Sykes Rymer wanted Tim to take over and he has. He was pleased when his twin grandsons were born and he wrote his O.G. for them, full of experience, wisdom and opinions when he said, "They are the next generation" – I think he meant – to farm. For Tim his boys have to plough their own furrows. There are eighteen grandchildren across John and Carol's families. As Tim was growing up in the '70's and early '80's to farm was the ambition of many, even those with little hope, or capital, to do so. As Ben and Josh have grown up farming has lost a lot of its charm to small boys for everything has become so big, health and safety regulations have restricted their ability to help on the farms in any worthwhile way. At school to be a farmer's boy is no longer a thing of envy, often more one of derision.

So the boys today show little inclination to farm and as far as Tim is concerned no matter for if, after a good broad education, they decide to go off in another direction so be it. If later they return then good. They will have to earn their position.

Tim Rymer is Chairman of a large international food company that is still family owned. As far as management goes then if the family is capable of carrying it onwards they should be welcome. If they don't wish to do so, or are incapable of so doing, then the Board will retain professional management.

21

Royal Agricultural Benevolent Institution

This book is a celebration of the life of one man who, in his lifetime, created a farming business that set the scene for change. It is fifty years ago that John Rymer bought his first farm, Eastburn Warren, near Driffield in East Yorkshire, 440 acres for £55/acre. Had he bought the farm ten years earlier it would have been for less and he would almost certainly have had to start his career with horses. As it was he and four men, with three very basic tractors, set to work to reach his goal of farming 1,000 acres; one day.

One man to 100 acres was the rule of thumb back in the 1950's and today twelve years on from John's death that figure is one man to 1,000 acres in the business he created. Productivity per man up ten fold and it goes even further because genetics and technology have lifted crop yields per acre to at least double during that time.

That first farm was on the edge of the village of Kirkburn, over the years the farm grew soon exceeding the original target and seventeen years on John had great satisfaction in buying the adjacent Southburn House, the main house in the area, with its surrounding estate. Over those twenty years the village was essentially an agricultural community and on the more remote Wold farms there were rows of cottages lived in by the sons of the soil, but today all that has changed. The labour force has shrunk, the village is now largely for commuters and the farm cottages are let to non-agricultural workers.

John was a great historian, which can be seen during a visit to Southburn Museum, he studied the 2,000 years of Wold farming development taking particular notice of the hey-days of "high farming" during the middle of the 19th Century when farms grew in size on the back of protectionist farming policies. However by 1860 rural depression had set in and farmers across the land were going out of business, through no fault of their own, but one man took their plight to heart.

Stoneground

John Mechi was an Essex farmer who had done well in the good years and had a farm that he knew could withstand the financial pressures that were bringing many others down. He knew something should be done and he wanted to put something back certain that others would follow his lead. So he wrote to the Times and from the one letter published he received over 700 letters of support for his idea of forming the R.A.B.I.

That was nearly 150 years ago when rural labour represented around 15% of the national workforce. Today that figure is down to 1.5% and over the last thirty years the rate of mechanisation and improving technology has seen a lot of farmers and their workers leave the industry. In 2004 British agriculture, in common with the rest of the EU, had the Government's support for cheap food, in the form of direct subsidies, removed which has resulted in a considerable speeding up in the reduction of the farm workforce. Many smaller farms have gone out of business putting the farmer, his family and, often, a worker out of work which, in an industry with an average age of sixty-two, has had serious repercussions. R.A.B.I. today hands out grants totalling £2.47 million to its beneficiaries as well as maintaining two residential homes. To do this they need to raise £4 million each year and they see their care being required even more over the next decade as farming changes continue to reduce labour as well as the number of farms.

The Institution operates on two fronts; first in Welfare Delivery and second in Wellbeing. The first includes continuous care, dealing with special situations such as disability and finally practical support for such things as household appliances. In their Wellbeing role they provide hampers, holidays and permanent homes for folk who can no longer live alone. The central office in Oxford is the nerve centre controlling twelve regional co-ordinators who provide local support which is not just about handing out money as in many cases they find that state benefits or local grants can solve the problems, but their 'clients' live rural lives often far removed from the urban centres where such things are commonplace. What they require is understanding advice on the availability of help and assistance and help with the inevitable form-filling.

John Rymer's Trust Fund has funded this book and the entire sales income will go to R.A.B.I. As I write the media are beginning to talk of the need to rebuild the food production industry in the UK, but sadly the workforce that is being forced out will not be required back, mechanisation has taken over. However the British countryside is still there and the work of those who are now no longer needed is the result of their labours, for that alone your support for them must be worthwhile.

Please give those who have fallen through the net of farming and food expansion your support. Thank you.

Acknowledgements

To be invited to write this book was a huge privilege, but at the time I accepted I certainly did not appreciate how involved I would become with John's life. It has been a unique experience and after looking at numerous ways of describing his life and times I hope that this one is the most accurate. John was a very gifted man with a wider range of talents than most people possess and he would have succeeded in most walks of life. However he shone as a food producer and led the way into attitudes and systems that have set the stage for the huge challenges that we now face as food supplies struggle to keep up with world population growth.

I could not have achieved this without the help and co-operation of Carol and Tim and it has often involved quite emotional moments as we have discussed their past lives. I thank them for asking me to do this in the first place and for their support over the last few months.

Chris Haskins wrote the Foreword early on and during our initial chat he gave me a most helpful guide to the way 'our man' was in his everyday life and in reading his tribute you will understand the relationship they had over the years together on the Company Board.

Ashley Burgess and I have known each other for many years and it came as a pleasant surprise for me to find that he had gone as 'bag carrier' with John on the Churchill Scholarship trip to Russia. They were quite different people going to an unknown land to peep behind the Iron Curtain. Both were involved in animal production one as a feed producer, the other a breeder and feeder of pigs. They were friends and with their families had sailed together on holidays, but Ashley felt he never fully knew John even after weeks together in a strange land. JSR was a very private man. An enjoyable lunch with Ashley gave me another angle on my subject for which I am very grateful.

John did though have one confidant and that was Pat Nutt who kindly read my final drafts, commenting and making suggestions, for which I thank him. He and John had similar standards of correctness and tidiness as important elements of any commercial farming business which put them on a par with one another and it was to Pat that John went when he simply wanted to talk. I suspect that the two touched on many subjects about which we will never know, but in the demanding life that John led they would have been important elements in founding and creating the Company.

As I have travelled around during this work I have met many who knew of John and a few who thought they knew him. Of one thing I am certain and that is a lot admired his success and leadership, but very few would have understood the complexity of the man. The man who really knew him would be rare.

Richard Fuller held a special place in the JSR team as he was a cattleman, but he is also renowned as a conservationist, an interest he integrates into the demands of commercial farm management so effectively. John admired this rare talent and had a love of walking Givendale with Carol throughout the seasons of the year. I would like to acknowledge especially Richard's help in getting some of the photographs in the book.

I have enjoyed putting this book together and I hope that you will get satisfaction in the knowledge that your purchase of it will go to help the many sons of the soil who have, through their work, made British land what it is today and what a tragedy it is that so many now find themselves cast out of the rural economy by the essential modernisation that has had to take place to meet the needs of the growing population.

Mike Keeble. Summer 2008.

1996 to 2008 The Legacy

As this book went to the printers in 2008 JSR Farms operate over 3,171 hectares of crops and grass which is very near to the acreage farmed back in 1982, but when John died that area stood at 4,272 hectares with a further 2,902 hectares farmed on contract. The Company was the largest family owned farming operation in the UK.

By 2007 the rotation had been simplified to meet ever rising costs and tighter margins. When John died in 1996 he was looking forward to the next phase of life with grandchildren, planting trees, tennis and those island breaks with Carol and , of course, he would have had that hand on the tiller which Tim may well have found a bit too firm.. Probably agriculture missed out as there can be little doubt that the " JSR Way " had a lot of experience behind it that would have been influential in the changes that were just coming over the horizon.

Across Europe food had become plentiful, food security had been forgotten and people became more interested in the how and the where of food production. There was a backlash against the wine lakes, the grain and butter mountains along with a sudden awareness that natural habitats had declined. In short the consumer became seduced by romantic rhetoric rather than the realism of economics. Subsidies had created a dependency culture and stifled efficiency dictated by market demands. However the Harrison philosophy that John adopted from the very start still prevailed; pigs, potatoes and peas which did not however take account of pig feed based on artificially high subsidised wheat prices.

The McSharry reform of the CAP started in 1992 with the introduction of unproductive set-a-side which, to the likes of John, was an anathema for there were 100m people starving around the World and the figure was rising. The talk in the JSR office was of producing wheat at £80/ tonne which would only be possible if the benefits of scale could be bought into play so it was a logical step for the

Company to offer contractual services to farms unable to achieve that all essential size.

With Tim in control the Arable Division launched JSR Contractual Services, but the Law of Unintended Consequences came into play when the Pound was unceremoniously dumped out of the Exchange Rate Mechanism. The devalued pound produced another four years of artificial prosperity for farming with a headlong rush by many farmers into the "contracting game". This bubble finally burst the very year that John died in 1996.

In March of that year BSE caused hysteria in the press when Professor Lacey of Leeds Universitypredicted that 500,000 people were about to die of CJD. Farming hit an all time low in the public perception and at the same time Monsanto launched GM tinned tomatoes onto the shelves ofSafeways supermarkets. That legacy still rolls on with Europe remaining virtually GM free while World starvation continues to climb. At the same time the global pig population exceeded demand level and the unsubsidised pig producer was about to feel the cold winds of globalisation.

Non-executive Director John Davies took the reins as full time Chairman in the period following the loss of the Founder allowing Tim time to run the JSR Healthbred business which had to adjust to the global situation—he faced a big challenge. The brand was strong both at home and abroad, but the arrangements that had been put in place were based on fixed fee royalties and this was limiting growth. Tim turned to the franchise system which would be a win win situation as both sides strived to maximise performance ,sales and profitability. Other competitors were able to get the use of JSR genetics and this was a worry, but the pigs were performing well and there were more pressing concerns.

In 1998 Tim took full control just as pig prices were at an all time low and swine fever had reared its head after an absence of many years. The ship he had inherited was in the eye of a storm and he secretly wished for that firm hand to return to the tiller for that was where John had shone.

He found that the business and the people he had inherited from his father were reluctant to tamper with his creation and there were quite a lot of sacred cows that had to be slain. Tim, who some regarded as the young pretender, had to face reality for things they were a changing and fast. Never before had farming had to face the full force of the global marketplace.

Three things were at the core of his concern. First with the pigs failing to meet their fixed costs debt was spiralling and the management costs were far too high, not least due to the fact that JSR were doing basic genetic improvements that were then benefiting competitors who in their turn were more competitive.

A strategic review was put in place as a matter of urgency with pig units being set a benchmark of 80p/kg production cost. The arable unit was spilt into roots and cereals with an £80/tonne production cost target. He also needed to get the right people into the right places for the show down ahead. Four non-executive directors played an incredible role in moving the company into a new phase over the next 7 years: Carol Rymer, Chris Haskins, Vincent Hedley-Lewis and Kevin Walker.

Onion processing was sold to the management, the farm across the Humber was sold back to the original vendors the Arden family and the pigs had to face up to a plethora of problems. The National herd reduced by 40%, swine fever hit in 1998, FMD in 2001 and 2007 and export bans were put in place .The Governments destruction of the once proud State Vet Service was costing the livestock industry dear.

Two competitors were taken over, Newsham in 1998 and Cotswold Pigs in 2001. They were integrated with some difficulty and surplus assets sold off.

In 2008 Tim can be proud of what he has achieved and he would be the first to admit that it has been a shared achievement with the Board and key staff. There is less land, but every hectare is farmed on a competitive basis and profits have never been better. Any contract farming is kept to within 20 miles and the seven arable managers of the past have been replaced by two specialist supervisors for roots and combinable crops. These are the real muddy boot men that John always hankered to be himself. Many of the breeding farms are now commercial units and all non core assets have been sold. The Result ?

Turnover is up, staff has reduced by 100 over 12 years, the debt ratio is low and in June 2007 the profit was £3mill.

The future is about a constant improvement in performance with the pig business having to maximise saleable meat sales per tonne of feed and to lift pig rearing to 25 pigs per sow per annum on all commercial units. Any failure to perform results in a can it be quickly fixed assessment and if not close it or sell it.

Growing cheap wheat to feed to pigs that have high value as breeding stock is still the core business, but that business has to be in balance with each of the other enterprises. The way that straw from the arable acres is processed into valuable organic manure is a simple example of the JSR recycling system that has gone for 50 years.

However balance is not a feature current EU or UK Agricultural policies. Food is secondary to environment, but as we celebrate 50 years of the "JSR Way" commodity shortages are suddenly hitting the headlines. We now need to achieve that all important balance between food and environmental stewardship.

What would John have made of it all? Tim knows just what he would have said, "You and the team have done well, but there are a few things I would disagree with." which is understandable for over 50 years there has been a double revolution and whereas for three hundred years we have been largely protected from globalisation we are now in the thick of it facing an exciting new era when food production, linked to energy production, will keep agriculture to the fore of world economics probably for evemore.

For Tim, his team and the Board there will be the challenges of change and they will succeed. John closed his O.G by saying that in 2013, when Tim will be 50, it will be his turn to record his life and times thus far. It is a sobering thought that all the forecasts suggest that the population bubble will burst in around 2040. That's not long in farming terms and Tim will only be 77.

As a result of Johns death Macmillan Nurses received bereavement donations of £100,000 as well as £9,700 from Carol and her sisters Southburn Christmas Fayre in that year. In 2007, the 14th Fayre, the sum raised was £21,941.

150 years in 2010
R·A·B·I
Supporting Farming Families

Celebrating 150 years of supporting the farming community

In 2010 the Royal Agricultural Benevolent Institution celebrates 150 years of unbroken service to those in need in the farming community. The amount of support provided varies from year to year, according to need, but it has continued to rise, reaching almost £2.5 million in 2007. This has only been possible through the generous support of those who are able to give, both financially and of their time.

How you can help?

Financial support for the work of RABI can take several forms. Donations and legacies are a vital source of funding, providing around 40% of the charity's annual income. Over the years bequests in wills, in the form of cash or property, have given RABI the capability to respond rapidly in times of crisis and to provide long-term support to elderly and disabled members of the farming community.

As a volunteer you can give as much or as little time as you wish to help RABI in your area. The support and enthusiasm of RABI's volunteers is crucial, not only for fundraising, but for raising awareness of its work, to both potential donors and beneficiaries.

Activities are coordinated on a local basis by regional officers and their volunteer county committees. By giving a little of your time, you will be helping some of the most vulnerable in farming - almost every community has at least one person who needs RABI's help.

From Westminster Abbey to York Minster

The achievements of RABI's first 150 years will be marked by a service of thanksgiving in Westminster Abbey in February 2010. This will herald a year of celebrations and events across England and Wales which will include a harvest festival in York Minster, in conjunction with the Yorkshire Agricultural Society; services of thanksgiving in Brecon, St Asaph and Truro Cathedrals; and conclude with a carol service in Dorchester Abbey, Oxfordshire, in December.

For full details of all RABI events and how you can help support those in need in our farming community, visit **www.rabi.org.uk** or contact RABI head office, Shaw House, 27 West Way, Oxford, OX2 0QH, phone 01865 724931.

For confidential help call the **RABI helpline** - **01865 727888.**

Registered charity no. 208858

Order Form

Stoneground is available by Mail Order, please send your order to:
JSR Limited, Southburn, Driffield, East Yorkshire YO25 9ED

Please send me .... copies at £10.00 each   £.....................

Postage & Packaging @ £1.50 per book   £.....................

Total enclosed   £.....................

Please make cheques payable to R.A.B.I.

Name ....

Address ....

....

Post code .... Tel. no. ....

Order Form

Stoneground is available by Mail Order, please send your order to:
JSR Limited, Southburn, Driffield, East Yorkshire YO25 9ED

Please send me .... copies at £10.00 each   £.....................

Postage & Packaging @ £1.50 per book   £.....................

Total enclosed   £.....................

Please make cheques payable to R.A.B.I.

Name ....

Address ....

....

Post code .... Tel. no. ....